# Higher
# Chemistry

# Higher Chemistry

**Dennis Garvie**  Principal Chemistry Teacher, Portobello High School, Edinburgh
**John Reid**  Principal Chemistry Teacher, Holy Rood High School, Edinburgh
**Anne Robertson**  Formerly Assistant Adviser in Science, Lothian Region

Oxford University Press

*Oxford University Press, Walton Street, Oxford OX2 6DP*

OXFORD  NEW YORK  TORONTO
DELHI  BOMBAY  CALCUTTA  MADRAS  KARACHI
PETALING JAYA  SINGAPORE  HONG KONG  TOKYO
NAIROBI  DAR ES SALAAM  CAPE TOWN
MELBOURNE  AUCKLAND

and associated companies in
BEIRUT  BERLIN  IBADAN  NICOSIA

*Oxford* is a trade mark of Oxford University Press

ISBN 0 19 914052 9

© Oxford University Press, 1978

First published 1978
Reprinted 1978, 1979, 1986

Printed in Hong Kong

# Preface

This book is intended to provide for the needs of pupils preparing for the S.C.E.E.B. Higher Chemistry examination. The content is an extension of the work covered in *Core Chemistry*, but we have reproduced certain passages from *Core Chemistry* rather than make references to a book which many pupils may not have.

The first section contains nine chapters of text and the second section contains experiments, most of which can be performed by the pupils. Each chapter contains a selection of questions taken from recent examinations, but teachers should be aware that although the selection of the questions was based on the relevant content, the questions themselves are very seldom testing recall of information. A complete list of abilities and skills being tested is contained in the S.C.E.E.B. syllabus.

Molecular equations have been used unless the chemistry requires the use of ionic equations, since pupils do tend to think in terms of 'moles of compound' from which 'moles of ions' may be deduced. The systematic naming of compounds has been continued from the style in *Core Chemistry* and we can only hope that the 'potassium permanganate brigade' will forgive us.

The evolution of oxygen and hydrogen in the electrolysis of sulphuric acid and sodium hydroxide solutions respectively has been dealt with in more detail than in *Core Chemistry* and the possibility of discharging water molecules has been used as a possible mechanism. However, the $E°$ values provided with these equations are theoretical values not experimental values. In an electrolytic cell the voltage used is usually so large that the $E°$ values are irrelevant.

Data provided in the appendices have been obtained from many sources and they do not necessarily correspond with the values in the S.C.E.E.B. Data Book. In some cases this may well be reflected in the answers to numerical problems.

We should like to acknowledge the help we have received in preparing this book from C. V. T. Campbell, Principal Lecturer in Chemistry at Moray House College of Education and from The Scottish Centre for Mathematics, Science and Technical Education at Dundee College of Education.

We also wish to thank the following for permission to use questions from their papers: the Scottish Certificate of Education Examination Board (marked SCEEB) and Pillans and Wilson Ltd. (marked P&W).

DG
JR
AMR

# Contents

# 1 Atomic theory

### 1.1 Atomic theory

Atoms are made up of small, sub-atomic particles called **protons, neutrons** and **electrons**. The protons and neutrons together make up the dense core of the atom called the **nucleus**. The electrons are very light, small particles which are situated around the nucleus. The probability of finding the electron is greatest within a certain volume about the nucleus. This volume is known as an **electron cloud** (Figure 1.1).

**Figure 1.1**

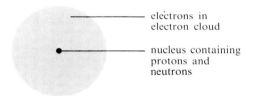

electrons in electron cloud

nucleus containing protons and neutrons

Because the masses of the atoms and the particles of which they are composed are so small, it is inconvenient to express them in the conventional unit of mass (kilogram). Instead these small masses are expressed in atomic mass units (a.m.u.): 1 a.m.u. $= 1.66 \times 10^{-27}$ kg. The relative masses of the sub-atomic particles are given in Table 1.1. Since atoms are electrically neutral, there must be an equal number of protons and electrons in an atom. The proton is assigned a charge of $1+$ and therefore the electron must have a charge of $1-$.

**Table 1.1** Summary of charge and mass of sub-atomic particles

| Particle | Relative mass (a.m.u.) | Charge | Approximate relative mass (a.m.u.) |
|---|---|---|---|
| Proton | 1.007 254 | $1+$ | 1 |
| Electron | 0.000 548 4 | $1-$ | 0 |
| Neutron | 1.008 613 | 0 | 1 |

### 1.2 Atomic number

The **atomic number** of an atom is the number of protons in the nucleus of that atom. This is one aspect of the structure of an atom which definitely identifies an element. Because atoms are electrically neutral, the atomic number will also be equal to the number of electrons. For example:

Atomic number of sodium = 11
Number of protons = 11
Number of electrons = 11

### 1.3 Mass number

The mass number is the sum of the protons and neutrons in an atom.

Mass number = number of protons + number of neutrons
From this:
Number of neutrons = mass number − number of protons
The information about an atom is often given in the way shown below:

Mass number →
$$Z \leftarrow \text{Symbol of the element}$$
Atomic number →

For example, an atom of chlorine, whose mass number is 35 and atomic number is 17, may be written as $^{35}_{17}Cl$. From this we can conclude the following:

1  Mass number       = 35
2  Atomic number      = 17
3  Number of protons   = 17
4  Number of electrons = 17
5  Number of neutrons  = 18

**Determination of the mass of the atom**

The instrument used to determine mass numbers is called the **mass spectrometer** and one is shown in Figure 1.2.
There are many different types of mass spectrometer, but they all operate on similar principles.

1  The element is vaporized.
2  The gas is bombarded by high energy electrons, which remove electrons from the atoms. The atoms then become positively charged particles.
3  These charged particles are projected into the magnetic field, where they are deflected according to their mass. The heavier particles will not be deflected as much as the lighter particles.
4  By varying the strength of the magnetic field, different masses can be made to pass through the slit. Each beam, on passing through the slit, strikes a collector plate where it acquires an electron to 'neutralize' each positive charge it contains. This produces a flow of current in the collector circuit which is amplified and recorded as a peak on a moving chart. The more electrons needed, the more current is produced, and the higher the peak on the recorder.

For example, magnesium, when analysed in the mass spectrometer, gives the trace shown in Figure 1.3. The trace shows that there are three different magnesium atoms present. One has a mass/charge ratio of 24, one a mass/charge ratio of 25 and one a mass charge ratio of 26. The bombarding electrons are given sufficient energy to remove one electron from each atom. Therefore we can assume that the charge of the deflected particle is 1 + . Thus we can say that magnesium contains atoms which have mass numbers of 24, 25 and 26, and that the atoms present are $^{24}_{12}\text{Mg}$, $^{25}_{12}\text{Mg}$, and $^{26}_{12}\text{Mg}$.

**Figure 1.2**

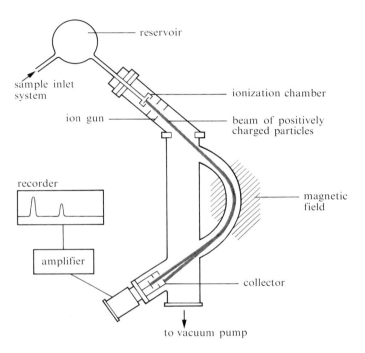

### 1.4 Isotopes

If we study the mass spectrometer trace that is obtained for magnesium (Figure 1.3),

**Figure 1.3**

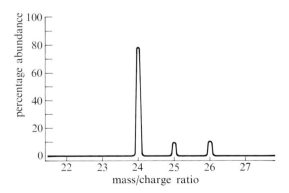

we can see that there are three peaks, each corresponding to different masses. In a sample of magnesium there are three species of atoms, each with its own mass number.

$^{24}_{12}Mg$; $^{25}_{12}Mg$; $^{26}_{12}Mg$

Atoms with the same atomic number, but with different mass numbers are known as **isotopes**.

### 1.5 Relative atomic mass (atomic weight)

The **relative atomic mass** of an element is the average mass of an atom of the element relative to the mass of the carbon 12 isotope, $^{12}_{6}C$, which has a mass of 12.000 00 a.m.u. The value of the relative atomic mass is determined from information obtained from the mass spectrometer.

**Example 1**   If we consider the graph shown in Figure 1.3, the isotopes present are $^{24}_{12}Mg$, $^{25}_{12}Mg$ and $^{26}_{12}Mg$ with abundances of 79 per cent, 10 per cent and 11 per cent respectively.

$$\text{Relative atomic mass} = \text{mass due to } ^{24}_{12}Mg + \text{mass due to } ^{25}_{12}Mg$$
$$+ \text{ mass due to } ^{26}_{12}Mg$$

$$= \frac{24 \times 79}{100} + \frac{25 \times 10}{100} + \frac{26 \times 11}{100}$$

$$= 18.96 + 2.50 + 2.86$$

$$= 24.32$$

The relative atomic mass of magnesium is 24.32.

**Example 2**   Gallium has two isotopes, $^{69}_{31}Ga$ and $^{71}_{31}Ga$, with abundances of 60 per cent and 40 per cent respectively.

$$\text{Relative atomic mass} = \text{mass due to } ^{69}_{31}Ga + \text{mass due to } ^{71}_{31}Ga$$

$$= \frac{69 \times 60}{100} + \frac{71 \times 40}{100}$$

$$= 41.4 + 28.4$$

$$= 69.8$$

The relative atomic mass of gallium is 69.8.

**Example 3**   The abundances of the isotopes of chromium are given in the table.

| Isotope | Abundance per cent |
|---|---|
| $^{50}_{24}Cr$ | 4 |
| $^{52}_{24}Cr$ | 84 |
| $^{53}_{24}Cr$ | 10 |
| $^{54}_{24}Cr$ | 2 |

Relative atomic mass = mass due to $^{50}_{24}Cr$ + mass due to $^{52}_{24}Cr$
+ mass due to $^{53}_{24}Cr$ + mass due to $^{54}_{24}Cr$

$$= \frac{50 \times 4}{100} + \frac{52 \times 84}{100} + \frac{53 \times 10}{100} + \frac{54 \times 2}{100}$$

$$= 2.00 + 43.68 + 5.30 + 1.08$$

$$= 52.06$$

The relative atomic mass of chromium is 52.06.

The abundances of the isotopes in any naturally occurring sample of an element are constant. Chemists require to know the relative atomic masses in order to calculate the quantities of reactants and products for the reactions they are carrying out in the laboratory.

## 1.6 Standards of relative atomic mass

At one time, the relative atomic masses were calculated by measuring the quantities of elements which would combine with each other.

The first standard used was hydrogen, as it was the lightest of all elements. By taking the mass of the hydrogen atom to be one unit, all other atoms therefore had nearly integral relative atomic masses. Later the hydrogen standard was replaced by oxygen.

Most of the elements' relative atomic masses were determined by combining them with oxygen. The hydrogen standard was later replaced by oxygen since any error in the relative atomic mass of oxygen, determined from the hydrogen standard, was transmitted to the elements.

Since the relative atomic mass of oxygen was nearly sixteen units on the hydrogen scale, it was assumed there was no error. It seemed logical to take the relative atomic mass of oxygen as sixteen units on the new scale. On that scale, the relative atomic mass of hydrogen was 1.08, and the relative atomic masses of many other elements were whole numbers which was very useful for chemists' calculations.

With the invention of the mass spectrometer came proof of the existence of isotopes and the realization that the oxygen standard was inadequate. Naturally occurring oxygen was shown to consist of a mixture of three isotopes, $^{16}_{8}O$, $^{17}_{8}O$ and $^{18}_{8}O$, the relative abundances of which were 99.76 per cent, 0.04 per cent and 0.20 per cent respectively. Chemists took the average value for the relative atomic mass as sixteen units, whereas physicists took the mass of the isotope $^{16}_{8}O$ as sixteen units. Obviously some compromise had to be reached as it was undesirable to have two 'standard' scales, even if they only differed to a very small degree. Following an international agreement in 1960, the modern practice is to use carbon as the standard. This scale, which takes the mass of the most commonly occurring isotope of carbon, $^{12}_{6}C$, to be twelve units exactly, has not altered the relative atomic masses of the elements by very much, but it means that there is now a scale which is accepted throughout the world. It is important to note two points at this stage. Firstly, the relative atomic mass scale is purely arbitrary. There is no reason why the present scale should not be superseded, sometime in the future, by a more convenient scale. Secondly, relative atomic masses have no units. This is because they are not actual masses of atoms, but rather that they are masses relative to the arbitrary standard.

### 1.7  Masses of molecules

The mass spectrometer is used to determine the mass of molecules. In this case, however, the ionized particles are molecules and fragments of molecules, which give rise to a larger number of peaks than might be expected.

Consider the mass spectrum of chlorine represented in Figure 1.4.

**Figure 1.4**

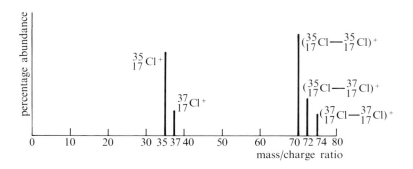

There are two isotopes of chlorine, $^{35}_{17}Cl$ and $^{37}_{17}Cl$. Three peaks are produced corresponding to all the possible combinations of chlorine atoms in the molecule and two peaks are produced corresponding to the fragments of the molecule.

If determining the relative atomic masses of the elements were the sole function of the mass spectrometer, the instrument would have outlived its usefulness. The main uses to which it is now put are determining the masses and the structures of organic compounds.

Consider the spectrum shown in Figure 1.5.

**Figure 1.5**

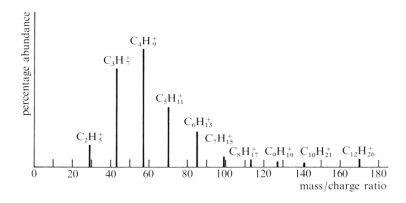

The spectrum indicates that the molecule has a molecular mass of 170 a.m.u. corresponding to $C_{12}H_{26}$. The fragments show that it is a linear molecule, since each peak differs by 14 a.m.u., which corresponds to the $CH_2$ group. It is in fact the mass spectrum of dodecane.

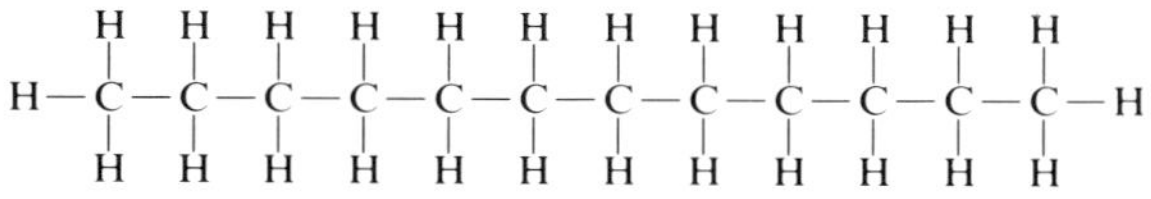

$$H-\overset{\displaystyle H}{\underset{\displaystyle H}{C}}-\overset{\displaystyle H}{\underset{\displaystyle H}{C}}-\overset{\displaystyle H}{\underset{\displaystyle H}{C}}-\overset{\displaystyle H}{\underset{\displaystyle H}{C}}-\overset{\displaystyle H}{\underset{\displaystyle H}{C}}-\overset{\displaystyle H}{\underset{\displaystyle H}{C}}-\overset{\displaystyle H}{\underset{\displaystyle H}{C}}-\overset{\displaystyle H}{\underset{\displaystyle H}{C}}-\overset{\displaystyle H}{\underset{\displaystyle H}{C}}-\overset{\displaystyle H}{\underset{\displaystyle H}{C}}-\overset{\displaystyle H}{\underset{\displaystyle H}{C}}-\overset{\displaystyle H}{\underset{\displaystyle H}{C}}-H$$

### Summary

From this chapter you should know:

1   Atoms are composed of protons and neutrons in a nucleus, which is surrounded by electrons.

2   The atomic number = number of protons = number of electrons.

3   The mass number = number of protons + number of neutrons.

4   How the mass number is determined.

5   Isotopes are atoms with the same atomic numbers but different mass numbers.

6   How to calculate the relative atomic mass of an element.

7   How and why the present standard for relative atomic mass was arrived at.

8   How the mass spectrometer can be used to determine the masses of molecules.

### Questions

1   The following table shows the mass numbers of the naturally occurring isotopes of the halogen elements:

| Element | Mass number of isotopes |
|---------|-------------------------|
| fluorine | 19 |
| chlorine | 35 |
|         | 37 |
| bromine | 79 |
|         | 81 |
| iodine | 127 |

1   Use this table and the relevant data on pages 184 to 185 to find support for the statement that 'the number of neutrons in the atomic nucleus tends to be even'.

**2**    The relative atomic mass of bromine is 80.0. What information does this give about the isotopes $^{79}Br$ and $^{81}Br$? *SCEEB*

**2**    Determine the relative atomic mass of element X which has three isotopes $^{28}_{14}X$, $^{29}_{14}X$ and $^{30}_{14}X$, their respective abundances being 92.2%, 4.7% and 3.1% *P & W*

**3**    **1**    Outline the operating principles of the mass spectrometer.
**2**    The trace shown was obtained, for an element A, from a mass spectrometer.

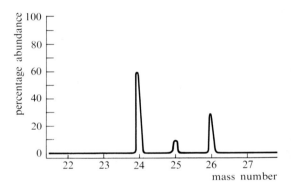

Calculate the relative atomic mass of A and identify it. *P & W*

**4**    **1**    Briefly explain how a mass spectrometer supplies evidence for the existence of isotopes.
**2**    Boron consists of two isotopes $^{10}B$ and $^{11}B$ with negligible traces of others.

| Isotope | Isotopic mass $^{12}C = 12.00$ | % |
|---|---|---|
| $^{10}B$ | 10.0 | 18.8 |
| $^{11}B$ | 11.0 | 81.2 |

Use this information to calculate the relative atomic mass of boron.
**3**    How many different types of HCl molecules are there? Which is the least abundant and which the most abundant type? *P & W*

**5**    The element calcium has a **relative atomic mass** of 40.8; its **atomic number** is 20 and there are several **isotopes**.
Point out ways in which the terms in heavy type are connected. *P & W*

6  1    Briefly outline the way in which the mass spectrometer works.
   2    An oxide of sulphur was analysed by mass spectrometry and the following diagram shows part of the trace obtained:

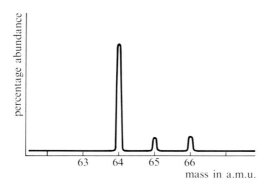

   **2.1**    Which oxide of sulphur was analysed?
   **2.2**    Explain the significance of the trace obtained. *P & W*

7    Various standards have been used in the calculation of relative atomic
masses. Name two of these and say why they are no longer used. *P & W*

8    A gaseous element, X, was analysed in the mass spectrometer and the
following information obtained:
$^{16}$X-abundance 93%
$^{17}$X-abundance 5%
$^{15}$X-abundance 2%
Calculate the relative atomic mass and identify it. *P & W*

9    An element X has three isotopes A, B, and C, which have the following
properties:

|   | % abundance | Mass number |
|---|---|---|
| A | 5 | 40 |
| B | 20 | 42 |
| C | 75 | 45 |

   1    What is the essential difference in the nuclear structure of these
isotopes?
   2    Calculate the relative atomic mass of X, correct to one decimal place.
*SCEEB*

# 2 Radioactivity

## 2.1 Discovery

If radiant energy falling upon a substance causes it to glow and the glow disappears when the energy is removed, this phenomenon is called fluorescence. In 1896 Henri Becquerel carried out experiments on the fluorescence of uranium compounds. He placed a uranium compound on a photographic plate which had been wrapped in black paper and exposed it to sunlight. He found that the plate darkened where the compound had been.

However, Becquerel observed later that a photographic plate, which had been in the same drawer as a uranium compound, seemed to have been exposed when he developed it. Since the plate had not been exposed to light, the uranium compound must have been emitting some kind of rays to cause darkening of the plate. His experiments confirming the phenomenon showed that it was not caused by fluorescence.

Figure 2.1 shows what happened when a key was placed on a covered, unexposed film, and a source with the same properties as those used by Becquerel was suspended above the film.

**Figure 2.1**

Pierre and Marie Curie continued Becquerel's study of these compounds. Marie Curie called the property of emitting these rays **radioactivity**. Using an ore of uranium, the Curies were able to isolate two new elements, polonium and radium, which were radioactive.

These discoveries were the beginning of the science of radiochemistry.

## 2.2 Types of radiation

Ernest Rutherford studied the penetrating power of radioactive emissions and discovered that uranium emitted two different types of radiation. Figure 2.2 is a representation of the experiment and the results obtained.

**Figure 2.2**

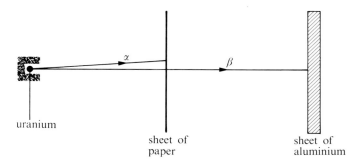

uranium

sheet of
paper

sheet of
aluminium

The type of radiation stopped by a sheet of paper was called alpha radiation ($\alpha$-radiation), and that which penetrated the paper but was stopped by a sheet of aluminium was called beta radiation ($\beta$-radiation).

Rutherford showed that the $\alpha$-radiation was composed of positively charged particles, **$\alpha$-particles**, which had a greater mass than hydrogen atoms. Rutherford and Royds sealed $\alpha$-particles inside a glass tube and after some time found that helium gas had formed. They concluded from this that $\alpha$-particles were helium nuclei which gained electrons from the air to form helium gas.

$$^4_2\text{He}^{2+} + 2e^- \rightarrow {^4_2}\text{He}$$

Becquerel carried out further experiments on $\beta$-rays and showed that they consisted of negatively charged particles with the same mass as an electron. The energy of these particles was, however, much greater than that of electrons and we can consider these **$\beta$-particles** as high energy electrons, $^0_{-1}e^-$.

A third type of radiation was discovered; this was called gamma radiation ($\gamma$-radiation). It did not have mass or charge but it was similar to X-rays with a much greater energy. It is a type of electromagnetic radiation.

The nature of the charges of the different types of radiation are shown in the diagram (Figure 2.3).

**Figure 2.3**

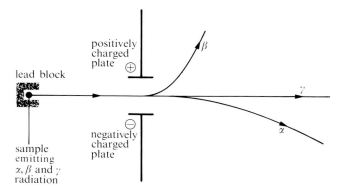

positively
charged
plate $\oplus$

lead block

$\beta$

$\gamma$

negatively
charged
plate $\ominus$

$\alpha$

sample
emitting
$\alpha, \beta$ and $\gamma$
radiation

As the radiations pass between the charged plates, deflection occurs according to charge. The $\beta$-particles deflect towards the positive plate, showing they are negatively charged, the $\alpha$-particles deflect towards the negative plate showing they are positively charged, and the $\gamma$-radiation is unaffected showing that it is not charged. Table 2.1 is a summary of the different types of radiation.

**Table 2.1**

| Radiation | Charge | Mass a.m.u. | Symbol |
|---|---|---|---|
| $\alpha$-particle | positive | 4 | $_2^4\text{He}^{2+}$ or $\alpha$ |
| $\beta$-particle | negative | 0 | $_{-1}^0e^-$ or $\beta$ |
| $\gamma$-radiation | zero | 0 | $\gamma$ |

## 2.3  Penetrating power of radiation

The different radiations have different energies and we would therefore expect differences in properties. One such property is the degree of penetration of the radiation. Figure 2.4 illustrates the penetrating power of $\alpha$, $\beta$ and $\gamma$ radiation.

**Figure 2.4**

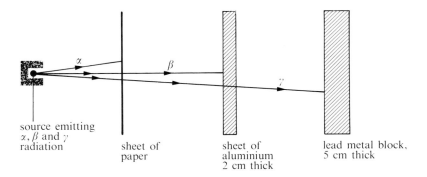

$\alpha$-particles are stopped by a sheet of paper and have a range of a few centimetres in air. $\beta$-particles are stopped by a sheet of aluminium and have a range of a few metres in air. $\gamma$-radiation has a range of about 100 metres in air and is stopped by about 5 centimetres of lead or concrete.

## 2.4  Measurement and detection of radioactivity

We must have some means of detecting radioactivity as the different kinds of radiation are not visible. One such instrument uses a Geiger-Müller tube (Figure 2.5).

**Figure 2.5**

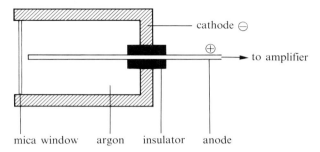

The Geiger-Müller tube is filled with argon with a central wire acting as an anode and an outer cylinder acting as a cathode. A high voltage is maintained between the anode and cathode and when $\beta$-particles or $\gamma$-rays ($\alpha$-particles if the mica window is very thin) enter the tube the argon atoms are ionized. The electrons formed discharge at the anode, and the positively charged argon ions discharge at the cathode. The resulting flow of electrons, after amplification, can be used to produce sound (as clicks), light flashes, or meter readings.

More sophisticated devices can both detect the radioactivity and measure the rate of emission as counts per second. The ratemeter illustrated in Figure 2.6 is such an instrument.

**Figure 2.6**

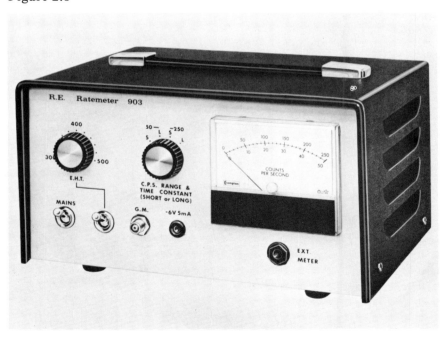

From measurements of the rate of radioactive decay, it was discovered that each radioactive element took a definite time to halve its amount of radioactivity.

## 2.5  Radioactive decay

The **half-life** of a radioactive substance is the time interval taken for the radiant species present to lose half its radioactivity. Each radioactive element has its own characteristic half-life. Table 2.2 gives some examples of half-lives and Figure 2.7 shows the rate at which $^{210}_{82}$Pb decays.

**Table 2.2**

| Element | Symbol | Half-life |
|---------|--------|-----------|
| Carbon | $^{14}_{6}$C | 5570 years |
| Uranium | $^{238}_{92}$U | $4.51 \times 10^9$ years |
| Radium | $^{224}_{88}$Ra | 3.64 days |
| Polonium | $^{216}_{84}$Po | $1.5 \times 10^{-1}$ seconds |
| Lead | $^{214}_{82}$Pb | 26.8 minutes |
| Lead | $^{210}_{82}$Pb | 22 years |
| Radon | $^{220}_{86}$Rn | 55 seconds |

**Figure 2.7**

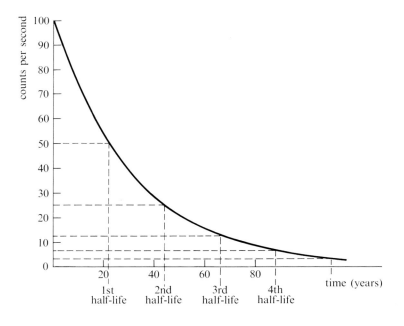

The half-life of $^{210}_{82}$Pb is 22 years. If the initial count of a sample of $^{210}_{82}$Pb is 100 counts s$^{-1}$ then after 22 years the count will be 50 counts s$^{-1}$. After a further 22 years the count will halve again to 25 counts s$^{-1}$.

Theoretically, a radioactive element never loses all its radioactivity, but for practical purposes we assume that it is negligible after seven half-lives.

## 2.6  Decay series

When radioactive elements decay, they emit radiation in the form of
$\alpha$-particles, $\beta$-particles and $\gamma$-rays. There is a fixed pattern of decay and this
is most easily illustrated by considering the decay of $^{242}_{94}Pu$ to $^{234}_{92}U$.

$^{242}_{94}Pu$ loses an $\alpha$-particle to form $^{238}_{92}U$

$$^{242}_{94}Pu \rightarrow {}^{238}_{92}U + {}^{4}_{2}He^{2+}$$

$^{238}_{92}U$ loses an $\alpha$-particle to form $^{234}_{90}Th$

$$^{238}_{92}U \rightarrow {}^{234}_{90}Th + {}^{4}_{2}He^{2+}$$

$^{234}_{90}Th$ loses a $\beta$-particle to form $^{234}_{91}Pa$

$$^{234}_{90}Th \rightarrow {}^{234}_{91}Pa + {}^{0}_{-1}e^{-}$$

$^{234}_{91}Pa$ loses a $\beta$-particle to form $^{234}_{92}U$

$$^{234}_{91}Pa \rightarrow {}^{234}_{92}U + {}^{0}_{-1}e^{-}$$

This series can be summarized as follows:

$$^{242}_{94}Pu \xrightarrow{-\alpha} {}^{238}_{92}U \xrightarrow{-\alpha} {}^{234}_{90}Th \xrightarrow{-\beta} {}^{234}_{91}Pa \xrightarrow{-\beta} {}^{234}_{92}U$$

There are several radioactive decay series:

e.g. the Actinium series:    $^{227}_{89}Ac \rightarrow {}^{207}_{82}Pb$

the Thorium series:    $^{234}_{90}Th \rightarrow {}^{208}_{82}Pb$

In any radioactive decay, there is no overall loss of mass. The total mass
at the beginning is the same as that at the end of any decay series. What
does change is the mass of radioactive substance. If we begin with 1g of
$^{235}_{89}Ac$, after one half-life the count will be halved and there will be 0.5g of
$^{235}_{89}Ac$ present but there will be 0.5g of other substances produced in the
decay.

### Table 2.3

| Time (half-lives) | Mass of $^{235}_{89}Ac$ (g) | Mass of other substances present (g) |
|---|---|---|
| 0 | 1.0000 | 0.0000 |
| 1 | 0.5000 | 0.5000 |
| 2 | 0.2500 | 0.7500 |
| 3 | 0.1250 | 0.8750 |
| 4 | 0.0625 | 0.9375 |

Note: The actual mass lost by the emission of particles is negligible as far
as masses measured on a laboratory balance are concerned.

### 2.7 Nuclear equations

As with chemical equations, so nuclear equations must balance; the total mass must be the same on left- and right-hand sides.

1    Consider the emission of an $\alpha$-particle from $^{218}_{84}Po$ to form $^{214}_{82}Pb$

$$^{218}_{84}Po \rightarrow \ ^{214}_{82}Pb + \ ^{4}_{2}He^{2+}$$

The number of protons on each side is 84, the total mass number on each side is 218. The only thing which has changed is the element.

2    Consider the emission of a $\beta$-particle from $^{214}_{82}Pb$ to form $^{214}_{83}Bi$

$$^{214}_{82}Pb \rightarrow \ ^{214}_{83}Bi + \ ^{0}_{-1}e^{-}$$

The difference in atomic number can be explained by considering the breakdown of a neutron $^{1}_{0}n$ to form a proton and an electron

$$^{1}_{0}n \rightarrow \ ^{1}_{1}H^{+} + \ ^{0}_{-1}e^{-}$$

In this way, a $\beta$-particle is emitted and the atomic number is increased by one.

### 2.8 Radioisotopes

While many radioisotopes occur in nature, means now exist to make new forms artificially and this is done on a large scale in the nuclear industry. Most artificial radioisotopes are produced by neutron bombardment of non-radioactive isotopes. Such isotopes are normally required for specific purposes.

1    *Agriculture*
Phosphate fertilizers are extensively used and it is, therefore, important to know how they function. The radioisotope $^{32}_{15}\overset{*}{P}$ is prepared

$$^{31}_{15}P + \ ^{1}_{0}n \rightarrow \ ^{32}_{15}\overset{*}{P}$$

and chemically combined into the fertilizer. Since it is radioactive, scientists can then study its distribution within plants. When used in this way, radioisotopes are known as *tracers*.

2    *Medicine*
Some radioisotopes have important uses in medicine because they are sources of $\gamma$-radiation, and as such are suitable for treatment of cancers.

(a) Radioactive gold needles are implanted in cancerous tumours

$$^{197}_{79}Au + \ ^{1}_{0}n \rightarrow \ ^{198}_{79}\overset{*}{Au}$$

The radioactive gold concentrates the radiation within the tumour for a short time since the half-life is only 2.7 days. In this way the patient is not exposed to radiation for a prolonged period of time.

(b) The radioisotope $^{60}\overset{*}{Co}$ has several uses.

$$^{59}_{27}Co + \ ^{1}_{0}n \rightarrow \ ^{60}_{27}\overset{*}{Co}$$

It is used for deep-seated cancerous growths which are inoperable, as it has a half-life of 5.29 years. As it is a source of $\gamma$-rays, it is also used to sterilize medical equipment.

(c) The thyroid gland in the human body regulates the metabolic rate of the body. As this gland is controlled by the amount of iodine it contains, any disorder can be detected by $^{131}_{53}I$.

$$^{127}_{53}I + 4^1_0n \rightarrow \,^{131}_{53}\overset{*}{I}$$

The half-life of iodine is 8 days. Therefore the patient would not be affected by prolonged exposure to the radioactivity.

　　This method can also be used to treat cancer of the thyroid as the radioactive isotope can be introduced into the gland without the use of surgery.

3　*Industry*

(*a*) $^{60}\overset{*}{C}o$ and other radioisotopes are used in industry to detect flaws in metals (Figure 2.8).

**Figure 2.8**　$\gamma$-radiograph of bevel wheel from the Great Clock ('Big Ben') at Westminster, showing previously undetected flaw.

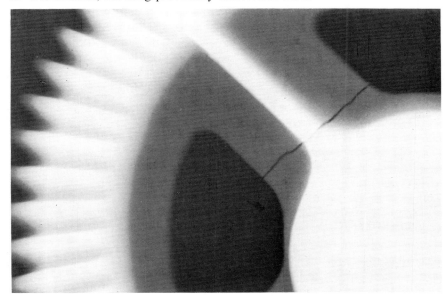

(b) Radioisotopes can be used to measure the thickness of paper, plastic and metal foils. Consider the diagram shown in Figure 2.9.

**Figure 2.9**

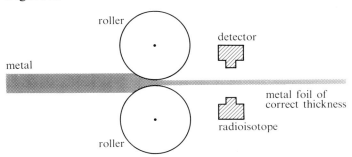

The rollers are arranged so that the metal foil is of the correct thickness. The radioisotope is emitting particles, some of which are being absorbed by the metal and the remainder are counted on the detector.

**If the count decreases.** This means the metal is absorbing more particles and is therefore, too thick. This information is passed through an electronic system and causes the rollers to come closer together.

**If the count increases.** This means the metal is not absorbing enough of the particles. It is therefore too thin and the rollers will then move farther apart.

### 2.9  Dating rocks, minerals and organic remains

(a)  Rocks and minerals

This method of dating depends on the presence of naturally occurring radioactivity. Pitchblende $U_3O_8$ is an ore of uranium. It is thought to have been formed when the Earth was formed. Analysis of samples of $U_3O_8$ shows that they all contain lead which has come from the decay of $^{238}_{92}U$.

We know that $^{238}_{92}U$ eventually decays to $^{206}_{82}Pb$, and we can use this decay series to date any rock or mineral which contains lead. If we assume that the sample was originally pure uranium then by measuring the present-day ratio of $^{238}U : ^{206}Pb$ in the sample we can calculate its age, using the half-lives of the members of the decay series. This type of calculation can be used to obtain some idea of the age of the Earth. It is found to be about five thousand million years.

(b)  Organic remains

This method of dating involves the radioisotope $^{14}_{6}\overset{*}{C}$, which is formed in the upper atmosphere by neutron bombardment of nitrogen.

$$^{14}_{7}N + ^{1}_{0}n \rightarrow ^{14}_{6}\overset{*}{C} + ^{1}_{1}H^+$$

The carbon then decays

$$^{14}_{6}\overset{*}{C} \rightarrow ^{14}_{7}N + ^{0}_{-1}e^-$$

and as $^{14}_{6}C$ has a half-life of 5570 years, it is suitable for dating organic remains. The method of carbon dating is based on the assumption that these two reactions have been occurring at a constant rate for the past 15 000 years.

All plants absorb carbon in the form of carbon dioxide during the process of photosynthesis.

$$6CO_2 + 6H_2O + energy \rightarrow C_6H_{12}O_6 + 6O_2$$

This carbon dioxide contains a small amount of $^{14}_{6}\overset{*}{C}O_2$. Carbon dioxide is taken into living things directly or indirectly by photosynthesis, and is given out from living things during respiration. The living system thus contains a constant amount of $^{14}_{6}\overset{*}{C}$. When a plant dies, it absorbs no more $^{14}_{6}\overset{*}{C}$, and that already present begins to decay. By comparing the amount of $^{14}_{6}\overset{*}{C}$ in organic remains with that present in a similar living plant, the age of the remains can be determined. Using this method, ages of up to 50 000 years can be calculated.

## 2.10 Nuclear fission

By 1934 an enormous amount of data had been accumulated about radio-activity and research workers like Fermi were trying to produce elements with atomic numbers greater than 92, by bombarding uranium with neutrons.

Hahn and Strassman bombarded uranium with neutrons and found that an unstable uranium atom was formed. Instead of producing an element with an atomic number greater than 92, the uranium atom broke down to form isotopes of barium and krypton and three neutrons.

$$^{235}_{92}U + {}^{1}_{0}n \rightarrow {}^{236}_{92}U \rightarrow {}^{141}_{56}Ba + {}^{92}_{36}Kr + 3{}^{1}_{0}n + \text{energy}$$

This process in which a heavy nucleus splits into two lighter ones is called **nuclear fission.**

The neutrons produced in this reaction can be used to bombard other atoms of $^{235}_{92}U$.

Thus bombardment by 1 neutron causes the production of three neutrons which will in turn bombard three $^{235}U$ atoms and produce 9 neutrons.

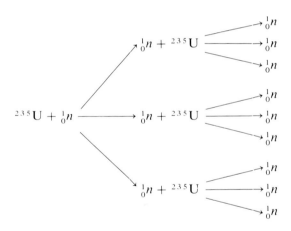

This kind of reaction is called a **chain reaction**.

In any nuclear fission a large amount of energy is released. This release of energy has now been harnessed in nuclear reactors which are used in power stations and nuclear submarines.

## 2.11 Nuclear fusion

This is the opposite of nuclear fission and occurs when two light nuclei combine to form a heavier nucleus. It is thought that fusion reactions of the type shown in the equation below occur in the sun.

$$^{2}_{1}H + {}^{2}_{1}H \rightarrow {}^{3}_{2}He + {}^{1}_{0}n$$

Fusion reactions release a huge amount of energy and this is the principle underlying the hydrogen bomb, the most devastating weapon yet invented.

**Summary**

From this chapter you should know:

1    The different types of radiation, $\alpha$, $\beta$ and $\gamma$.

2    An $\alpha$-particle is ${}_2^4\text{He}^{2+}$ and a $\beta$-particle is ${}_{-1}^{0}e^{-}$.

3    The penetrating power of $\alpha$-, $\beta$- and $\gamma$-radiation.

4    How radiation is detected and measured.

5    Radioactive elements decay at a fixed rate, called the half-life.

6    There are natural decay series.

7    How to construct a nuclear equation.

8    How radioisotopes are formed and their uses.

9    Rocks, minerals and organic remains can be dated by means of radioactive decay.

10   The difference between nuclear fission and nuclear fusion.

**Questions**

1    The graph shows the variation with time of the intensity of radiation due to the decay of a 10 g sample of ${}^{210}\text{Po}$. Copy the graph into your answer book (no graph paper required) and add a dotted line to show what the graph would be for a 5 g sample of ${}^{210}\text{Po}$. *SCEEB*

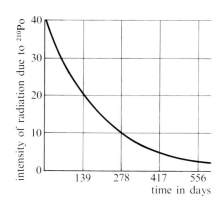

2    What are the species $x$ and $y$?
1    ${}_{11}^{24}\text{Na} \rightarrow x + {}_{-1}^{0}e^{-}$
2    ${}_3^6\text{Li} + y \rightarrow {}_1^3\text{H} + {}_2^4\text{He}^{2+}$   *SCEEB*

3    From *Structure of the atom* by Sir E. Rutherford (1914).
'In the following table the atomic weight and the nucleus charge are given for a few of the successive elements arising from the transformation of uranium. The actual charge of uranium is unknown, but for simplicity it is assumed to be 100.

| Successive elements | $\mathrm{Ur_1}$ | $\xrightarrow{(1)}$ | $\mathrm{UrX_1}$ | $\xrightarrow{(2)}$ | $\mathrm{UrX_2}$ | $\xrightarrow{(3)}$ | $\mathrm{Ur_2}$ | $\xrightarrow{(4)}$ | Io | $\xrightarrow{(5)}$ | Ra |
|---|---|---|---|---|---|---|---|---|---|---|---|
| Atomic weights | 238.5 | | 234.5 | | 234.5 | | 234.5 | | 230.5 | | 226.5 |
| Charge on nucleus | 100 | | 98 | | 99 | | 100 | | 98 | | 96 |

Following the recent theories, it is supposed that the emission of an $a$-particle lowers the nucleus charge by two units, while the emission of a $\beta$-particle raises it by one unit.

It is seen that $\mathrm{Ur_1}$ and $\mathrm{Ur_2}$ have the same nucleus charge although they differ in atomic weight by four units.

If the nucleus is supposed to be composed of a mixture of hydrogen nuclei with one charge and helium nuclei with two charges, it is, *a priori*, conceivable that a number of atoms may exist with the same nucleus charge but of different atomic masses. The radioactive evidence certainly supports such a view, but probably only a few of such possible atoms would be stable enough to survive for a measurable time.'

1    Which of the steps (1) to (5) involve release of an $a$-particle? Which involve loss of a $\beta$-particle?

2    Using only evidence contained in the passage, show how you can deduce the nature of the $a$-particle.

3    What information contained in the passage might lead Rutherford to decide that the helium nucleus is a fundamental particle in the nucleus?

4    Use data relating to some of the elements between lithium and neon to support the idea that the helium nucleus is a fundamental building-block in the nuclei of other atoms.

5    Is there support in the information given in the passage for the idea that the hydrogen nucleus is a basic unit in the structure of atomic nuclei? (Give your reasoning.)

6    What evidence in the passage suggests that the nucleus cannot be built up of hydrogen and helium nuclei only? *SCEEB*

4    The following reactions occur during nuclear fission:

$$^{235}_{92}\mathrm{U} + {}^{1}_{0}n \rightarrow {}^{236}_{92}\mathrm{U}$$

$$^{236}_{92}\mathrm{U} \rightarrow {}^{90}_{36}\mathrm{Kr} + {}^{144}_{56}\mathrm{Ba} + 2{}^{1}_{0}n$$

Explain how a very rapid reaction could result from this. *SCEEB*

5    Use the half-lives in Table 2.2 on page 14 to answer the following:

$$^{224}_{88}\mathrm{X} \xrightarrow{(i)} {}^{220}_{86}\mathrm{Y} \xrightarrow{(ii)} {}^{216}_{84}\mathrm{Z}$$

1    Name the elements represented by X, Y and Z.

2    Name the particle emitted in stage (i).

3    Which element in the series shown above has the shortest half-life? *SCEEB*

6    A method of archaeological dating is based on the properties of the isotope carbon-14. Ordinary carbon atoms are nearly all of atomic mass 12, but one atom in every million million has the atomic mass 14. Both isotopes undergo identical chemical reactions, including photosynthesis, respiration etc., but the atoms of carbon-14 emit low energy $\beta$-rays which even when present in very small amounts can be detected by means of a sensitive Geiger-Müller counter.

Carbon-14 atoms are being constantly formed in the upper atmosphere by the reaction of nitrogen with neutrons and continuously decaying into nitrogen, at the rate of half of them disappearing in about 5000 years, so that in the atmosphere and in all living matter there is a fixed proportion of carbon-14. Once the living matter has died, however, it is no longer obtaining fresh supplies of carbon-14 by photosynthesis or by eating plants which have photosynthesized.

The carbon-14 method has given results which agree well with the specimens of known age such as objects found in the Pyramids but it cannot be used for remains which are more than about 50 000 years old.

1    Explain why the concentration of radioactive carbon remains constant during the life of the organism.
2    Indicate clearly the difference in structure between the two isotopes of carbon.
3    What is the evidence in the passage that carbon-14 is a radio-isotope?
4    Write an equation to represent the formation of the radio-isotope carbon-14 in the atmosphere.
5    Write an equation to represent the radioactive decay of carbon-14.
6    What is the half life of carbon-14?
7    What fraction of the original radioactivity would remain in a sample of wood 50 000 years old?
8    Why can this method of dating not be used for remains which are more than 50 000 years old?
9    What is the evidence in the passage for the alchemists' dream of transmutation?
10    What does the passage suggest is the major advantage of detection and measurement involving radio-isotopes over normal chemical methods?
11    The age of clothing found in archaeological 'digs' can be determined by carbon dating; that of diamond jewellery cannot. Give an explanation.
*SCEEB*

7    $^{10}_{5}B + ^{1}_{0}n \rightarrow ^{p}_{q}X + 2^{4}_{2}He$

What are the values of $p$ and $q$ in the above equation? What is element X?
*SCEEB*

8    A solution of X-nitrate was found to be emitting both $\alpha$ and $\beta$-particles. The addition of sodium hydroxide solution produced a precipitate of X-hydroxide. After filtration it was shown that the residue emitted only $\alpha$-particles while the filtrate emitted only $\beta$-particles. Further investigation showed that the filtrate contained ions of $^{228}Ra$. After some time it was found that the residue was emitting $\beta$-particles in addition to $\alpha$-particles.
1    What are $\alpha$- and $\beta$-particles?
2    Explain why the residue started to give evidence of $\beta$-particle emission after some time.

3    Give the name, mass number and atomic number of
   **3.1**    element X
   **3.2**    the product formed when $^{228}$Ra emits a $\beta$-particle.
4    How would the half-life of $10^{-3}$ g of element X compare with the
half-life of an equal weight of X-hydroxide? Explain your answer.
5    Explain which reagent you would choose in order to obtain a radioactive precipitate from a solution containing ions of $^{228}$Ra.
Write an ionic equation for the precipitation reaction. *P & W*

9    **1**    Shown below is the type of graph obtained when the mass of a radioactive isotope decaying is plotted against time.

Explain why the graph has this shape.
Using graph paper, find how much of a piece of uranium weighing 10 g
will decay during $6.75 \times 10^9$ years. The half-life of uranium is $4.5 \times 10^9$
years.
**2**    Explain why the loss of an $\alpha$-particle causes a displacement of two
places to the left in the Periodic Table.
What displacement is caused by $\beta$-particle emission? *P & W*

# 3 Kinetic theory and Avogadro

### 3.1 Ideal gases and real gases

In the early part of the course, we carried out a number of experiments to establish the theory that matter was made up of minute particles, and it may be worth recalling some of them concerned with gases.

**Looking at smoke in a smoke-cell**
The particles of smoke are seen to move about in a completely random way, which is called Brownian motion after Robert Brown who first observed the random movement of pollen in water. We explain this movement of the smoke particles by saying that they are being constantly bombarded by smaller invisible particles of air.

**Diffusion of a smell**
When a bottle of perfume is opened, everyone in the room is able to smell it within a short time without any liquid being taken from the bottle. The explanation is that some of the particles of perfume diffuse through the air until they fill the room.

**Bicycle pump**
The piston can be pushed in, even when your finger covers the outlet hole. When the piston is released, it springs back to its original position. Gases can be compressed and we explain this in terms of pushing the particles closer together. We are also aware of the increase in pressure due to the particles colliding with the cylinder and piston more often.

**Heating a gas**
A flask full of air at room temperature is at the same pressure as the atmosphere, but when it is warmed, an increase in pressure is observed. To account for this we assume that the particles are moving faster at the higher temperature causing more collisions per second.

The kinetic theory of gases makes the following assumptions about an ideal gas:

1 Gases consist of tiny particles of negligible volume.
2 The particles are in rapid linear motion in all directions.
3 All collisions are perfectly elastic, i.e. no energy is lost.
4 The particles do not attract each other.

For **real gases**, not all of these conditions apply. Gases like argon, neon and hydrogen, with very small molecules will approximate to these conditions but larger molecules like carbon dioxide and propane will show deviations from the behaviour expected of an **ideal gas**, particularly because of increased forces of attraction between the molecules.

### 3.2 Boyle's Law

The volume of a fixed mass of gas is inversely proportional to the pressure, *provided the temperature is constant*.

Although we are all aware of the fact that an increase in pressure causes the volume of gas to decrease, the condition for a proportionality statement requires that a graph of one variable against the other is a straight line through the origin.

**Figure 3.1**

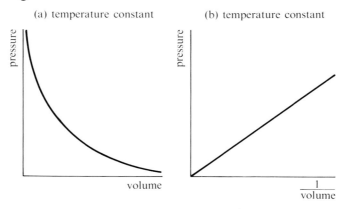

(a) temperature constant          (b) temperature constant

From Figure 3.1, $P \propto \dfrac{1}{V}$     ($T$ constant)

The proportionality can be written as an equality if we introduce a constant $k$.

$$P = \frac{k}{V} \quad \text{or} \quad PV = k.$$

This is an extremely useful relationship since it enables us to calculate the volumes of a fixed mass of gas under new conditions of pressure, provided the temperature is kept constant.

$$k = P_1 V_1 = P_2 V_2 = P_3 V_3 = \cdots$$

**Example 1**  A sample of gas occupied 390 cm³ at a pressure of 760 mm of mercury. Calculate the volume it would occupy at 780 mm of mercury if the temperature remains constant.

$$P_1 V_1 = P_2 V_2 \quad (T \text{ constant}).$$
$$760 \times 390 = 780 \times V_2$$
$$V_2 = \frac{760 \times 390}{780} \text{ cm}^3 = 380 \text{ cm}^3$$

**Example 2**  What pressure would be required to compress 7.75 litres of hydrogen at atmospheric pressure to 5 litres?

$$P_1 V_1 = P_2 V_2 \quad (T \text{ constant})$$
$$1 \times 7.75 = P_2 \times 5$$
$$P_2 = \frac{1 \times 7.75}{5} \text{ atm} = 1.55 \text{ atm}$$

**Note on units of pressure**

1  In the laboratory, chemists are often working with glass vessels and consequently they are usually dealing with gases at pressures in the region of atmospheric pressure. The most convenient way of measuring such pressures is to use a manometer and simply measure the height of the mercury column in millimetres.

The **standard atmospheric pressure** is taken as 760 mmHg.

Some chemists give this unit mmHg the name torr after the Italian scientist Torricelli.

1 atm = 760 mmHg = 760 torr

2  In industrial processes where large pressures are often used, it is more convenient to use the atmospheric unit, e.g. the Haber process operates at about 200 atm.

3  From a theoretical point of view a unit of pressure ought to be expressed as a unit of force per unit of area, and indeed many data books express pressure in newton per square metre ($N\ m^{-2}$) which is also called the pascal (Pa).

1 atm = $1.01 \times 10^5$ Pa

Boyle's Law holds for all units of volume and pressure, provided the same units are used on both sides of the equation.

**3.3  The relationship between volume and temperature**

When solids and liquids are heated, they expand but they all expand by different amounts for the same amount of heat supplied. You will have carried out some experiments in your science course at some stage to illustrate these points. In 1787 a French scientist, Charles, discovered that for gases, the volume increased by a factor of $\dfrac{1}{273}$ for each Celsius degree rise in temperature, and that this was true for all gases. This means that if we draw a graph of volume against temperature for a fixed mass of gas, a straight line is obtained provided the pressure is kept constant.

Volume at 1°C        $V_1 = V_0 + \dfrac{1}{273} V_0$

Volume at 10°C        $V_{10} = V_0 + \dfrac{10}{273} V_0$

If we draw a graph of volume against temperature we get a straight line, but we have an intercept $V_0$ at 0°C. To get a straight line through the origin, we simply move the volume axis back to the point where the graph meets the temperature axis. You ought not to be too surprised to find the new origin at $-273$°C.

Temperatures measured from this new origin are called absolute temperatures and the scale is called the Kelvin scale after Lord Kelvin. It was he who first suggested from theoretical considerations the existence of an absolute zero of temperature.

**Figure 3.2**

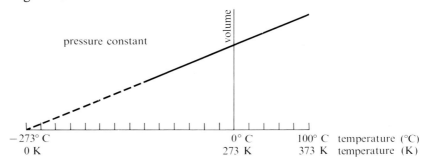

pressure constant

−273° C         0° C     100° C   temperature (°C)
0 K          273 K    373 K   temperature (K)

**Charles' Law**    The volume of a fixed mass of gas is directly proportional to the absolute temperature provided the pressure is kept constant.

$$V \propto T \qquad (P \text{ constant})$$

$$V = k_1 T \qquad \text{where } k_1 \text{ is a constant}$$

$$k_1 = \frac{V_1}{T_1} = \frac{V_2}{T_2} = \frac{V_3}{T_3} \qquad (P \text{ constant})$$

This relationship enables us to calculate the volume of a given mass of gas at different temperatures provided the pressure is kept constant. The **standard temperature** is taken as 273 K.

**Example 1**    What volume would be occupied by a given sample of gas at 100°C if it occupied 50 cm³ at 0°C? Assume that the pressure is constant.

$$\frac{V_1}{T_1} = \frac{V_2}{T_2}$$

$$\frac{50}{273 \text{ K}} = \frac{V_2}{373 \text{ K}}$$

$$V_2 = \frac{50 \times 373}{273} \text{ cm}^3 = 68 \text{ cm}^3.$$

**Example 2**    A given sample of gas occupies 20 cm³ at 20°C. At what temperature will it have doubled its volume? Assume constant pressure.

$$\frac{V_1}{T_1} = \frac{V_2}{T_2}$$

$$\frac{20}{293} = \frac{40}{T_2}$$

$$T_2 = \frac{40 \times 293}{20} = 586 \text{ K} = 313°C.$$

### 3.4  General Gas Equation

In most experiments in the laboratory, it is inconvenient to hold one of the variables constant. Charles' Law and Boyle's Law can be combined to give a general equation

$$k_2 = \frac{P_1 V_1}{T_1} = \frac{P_2 V_2}{T_2} = \frac{P_3 V_3}{T_3}$$

**Example 1**    The volume of hydrogen collected in a displacement reaction between zinc and dilute acid was 236 cm³, measured at the room conditions of 20°C and 720 mmHg. Calculate the volume of hydrogen at standard temperature and pressure (s.t.p.).
Substitute the s.t.p. conditions on one side and the experimental conditions on the other.

$$\frac{P_1 V_1}{T_1} = \frac{P_2 V_2}{T_2}$$

$$\frac{760 V_1}{273} = \frac{720 \times 236}{293}$$

$$V_1 = \frac{273 \times 720 \times 236}{293 \times 760} \text{ cm}^3 \approx 208 \text{ cm}^3$$

The volume of hydrogen liberated is 208 cm³ at s.t.p.

**Example 2**    In devising an experiment, a chemist calculated that the volume of gas evolved would be 40 cm³ at s.t.p. He was hoping to collect the gas in a burette with a 50 cm³ scale at room conditions which were 780 mmHg and 19°C. Will the burette collect the gas successfully?

(s.t.p.)    $\dfrac{P_1 V_1}{T_1} = \dfrac{P_2 V_2}{T_2}$    (experimental)

$$\frac{760 \times 40}{273} = \frac{780 V_2}{292}$$

$$V_2 = \frac{760 \times 40 \times 292}{273 \times 780} \text{ cm}^3 \approx 42 \text{ cm}^3.$$

The burette will be suitable for the experiment.

**For 1 mole of gas**    $\dfrac{P_1 V_1}{T_1} = R$ where $R$ is the universal gas constant.

The implication of this equation is that the volume of 1 mole of an ideal gas at s.t.p. should be constant

$$V = \frac{R T_1}{P_1} = \frac{R T_2}{P_2}$$

We can put this to the test if we calculate the volume occupied by 1 mole of some *real* gases at s.t.p. from measurement of their densities, i.e. the mass of a given volume.

**Table 3.1**

| Gas | Formula | Mole (g) | Density at s.t.p. (g $l^{-1}$) | Volume of the mole (l) |
|---|---|---|---|---|
| Hydrogen | $H_2$ | 2.02 | 0.0899 | 22.4 |
| Helium | He | 4.00 | 0.179 | 22.4 |
| Nitrogen | $N_2$ | 28.00 | 1.25 | 22.4 |
| Oxygen | $O_2$ | 32.00 | 1.43 | 22.4 |

The volume occupied by a mole of gas at s.t.p. is 22.4 litres, the **molar volume**.

### 3.5 Avogadro's law and the mole

Gay-Lussac noticed that when gases react, the volumes in which they do so are simply related to each other, and also to the volumes of the products if they are gaseous. The volumes are, of course, measured under the same conditions of temperature and pressure.

For example:

Two volumes of hydrogen combine with one volume of oxygen to form two volumes of steam.

Three volumes of hydrogen combine with one volume of nitrogen to form two volumes of ammonia.

John Dalton was unable to explain these results because he assumed that equal volumes of gases contained equal numbers of atoms and therefore, he would have expected only one volume of steam and one volume of ammonia respectively. The error in his reasoning was his assumption that the particles of gas were atoms. Avogadro distinguished between atoms and molecules and he proposed that equal volumes of gases under the same conditions of temperature and pressure, contained equal numbers of molecules. This is **Avogadro's Hypothesis.** It has been established by experiment that 22.4 l of any gas at s.t.p. contains one mole of that gas. Boyle's Law and Charles' Law lead us to suppose that if the volume and temperature of a mole of gas are fixed then the pressure will be the same for all gases, and in kinetic terms we take this to mean that the number of molecules is the same for each. What is required now is experimental evidence to support this line of argument. Rutherford and Royds devised an experiment to count the number of particles in a fixed volume of gas and they then went on to calculate the number of molecules in a mole.

### 3.6 The nature of $a$-particles

Rutherford and Royds used the apparatus shown diagrammatically in Figure 3.3. The sample of radon gas in the inner tube emits $a$-particles which penetrate the thin glass wall and enter the outer tube. A spark across the electrodes gives the atomic spectrum of the $a$-particles. A Geiger counter is used to count the number of emissions: The volume of gas in the outer tube can be measured after a suitable time interval.

**Figure 3.3** Rutherford and Royds' experiment

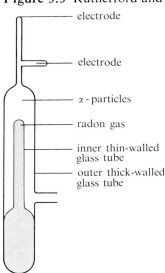

1   The atomic spectrum of the $\alpha$-particles corresponded to that of helium gas, indicating that $\alpha$-particles are $^4_2\text{He}^{2+}$
2   The volume of the helium gas ions was found to be $7.34 \times 10^{-3}$ cm$^3$ at 292 K and 745 mmHg.
3   The number of $\alpha$-particles emitted was $1.82 \times 10^{17}$.

From the experiment:

$$\text{Volume of helium at s.t.p.} = \frac{273 \times 745 \times 7.34 \times 10^{-3}}{760 \times 292} \text{ cm}^3$$

$$= 6.72 \times 10^{-3} \text{ cm}^3$$

$$= 6.72 \times 10^{-6} \text{ l.}$$

Also $6.72 \times 10^{-6}$ l of helium contain $1.82 \times 10^{17}$ particles

$$\therefore \quad 22.4 \text{ l of helium contain} \frac{1.82 \times 10^{17} \times 22.4}{6.72 \times 10^{-6}} \text{ particles}$$

$$= 6.06 \times 10^{23} \text{ particles.}$$

A mole of helium contains $6.06 \times 10^{23}$ atoms (monatomic molecules).

### 3.7 Faraday's laws of electrolysis

Faraday measured the charge required to liberate given volumes of gases, He also measured the masses of solids liberated at electrodes in the process of electrolysis. Although the original statements of the laws are in terms which are inappropriate to the system of units used in this book, they show that the quantity of electricity required to discharge a mole of atoms of an element is a simple multiple of 96 500 coulombs. The results of one such experiment are given below.

**Note about units**  An ammeter reading measures the number of coulombs of charge per second.

$$\text{amps} = \frac{\text{coulombs}}{\text{seconds}}$$

**The charge to deposit 1 mole**  To measure the charge supplied by a source, we have to measure the current and the time for which it passes. Hence the charge is given by

$$\text{coulombs} = \text{amps} \times \text{seconds}$$

$$Q = I \times t.$$

**Figure 3.4** Quantitative electrolysis.

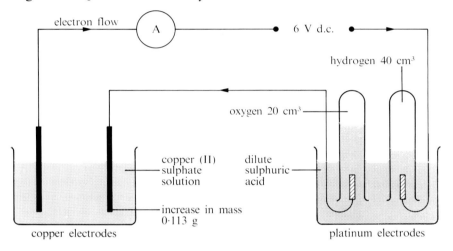

Results

$$\text{Current} = 0.2 \text{ A}$$
$$\text{Time} = 1720 \text{ s}$$
$$Q = 0.2 \times 1720 = 344 \text{ coulombs}$$
$$\text{Volume of H}_2 = 40 \text{ cm}^3$$
$$\text{Volume of O}_2 = 20 \text{ cm}^3$$
$$\text{Mass of Cu deposited} = 0.113 \text{ g}$$

Table 3.2 shows the quantity of electricity required to deposit 1 mole of the above elements.

**Table 3.2**

| Element | 1 mole | Charge to deposit 1 mole |
|---------|--------|--------------------------|
| Hydrogen | 22.4 l | $2 \times 96\,500$ C |
| Oxygen | 22.4 l | $4 \times 96\,500$ C |
| Copper | 63.5 g | $2 \times 96\,500$ C |

By carrying out experiments of the kind shown here, it is possible to obtain results for a range of elements. Since 96 500 coulombs is a frequently used factor, it was called the faraday (F) after the scientist, so that 1 F = 96 500 C.

| Element | 1 mole | Charge to deposit 1 mole (F) |
|---------|--------|------------------------------|
| Ag | 108 g | 1 |
| Na | 23 g | 1 |
| K | 39 g | 1 |
| $H_2$ | 22.4 l | 2 |
| $O_2$ | 22.4 l | 4 |
| $Cl_2$ | 22.4 l | 2 |
| Cu | 63.5 g | 2 |
| Al | 27.0 g | 3 |
| Fe | 55.8 g | 2 from $Fe^{2+}$, 3 from $Fe^{3+}$ |

### 3.8 The charge on a single electron

There is a simple relationship between the charge 96 500 coulombs and the mole. If we knew the actual charge on an electron in coulomb units, we could then find the number of electrons corresponding to 96 500 C and hence we could deduce the number of particles in a mole. This was the reasoning which led Millikan to devise the Oil Drop Experiment.

**Figure 3.5** Oil drop experiment

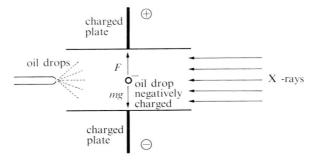

X-rays cause ionization of oxygen and nitrogen molecules and some of the 'free' electrons are picked up by the oil drop. There are two forces acting on the charged drop:

1. the downward pull of gravity, and
2. the upward pull of the electric field.

It is theoretically possible to adjust the electric field to hold the oil drop steady in space. The opposing forces are now equal and opposite. By equating the forces, the charge on the oil drop can be calculated.

$$mg = \frac{eV}{d}$$    where    $m$ is the mass of the drop in kg.
$g$ is the acceleration due to gravity in m s$^{-2}$
$e$ is the charge on the oil drop in coulombs

$$\therefore \quad e = \frac{mgd}{V} \text{ C}$$

$V$ is the voltage
$d$ is the distance between the plates in m.

Millikan found that the charge on the oil drop was (within experimental error) an integral multiple of $1.6 \times 10^{-19}$ C, and this was the smallest common factor. He therefore assumed that the charge on a single electron was $1.6 \times 10^{-19}$ C.

From Faraday's experiments, we know that it requires 96 500 C to discharge one mole of hydrogen ions.

$$H^+(aq) + e \rightarrow \tfrac{1}{2}H_2(g).$$

The number of electrons represented by $e$ in Millikan's equation is

$$\frac{96\,500}{1.6 \times 10^{-19}} = 6.03 \times 10^{23}$$

A mole of hydrogen ions must therefore contain $6.03 \times 10^{23}$ ions, and a mole of hydrogen gas must contain $6.03 \times 10^{23}$ molecules.

### 3.9 Avogadro's Number $N_A$

This number ($6 \times 10^{23}$) represents the number of particles in a mole of a substance. It is sometimes called Avogadro's constant. The **mole** can now be regarded as an Avogadro's Number of the appropriate particles. This is the important bridge that enables us to change statements about moles of elements and compounds (quantities which can be measured in a laboratory) to statements about the atoms and molecules themselves. Consider the combustion of hydrogen in oxygen.

$$2H_2(g) + O_2(g) \rightarrow 2H_2O(l)$$

Two moles of hydrogen combine with one mole of oxygen to form two moles of water.

If each mole contains $6 \times 10^{23}$ molecules, then two molecules of hydrogen combine with one molecule of oxygen to form two molecules of water.

**Example 1** What volume measured at s.t.p. of carbon dioxide would be liberated by the action of heat on 50g of calcium carbonate? How many molecules of carbon dioxide does this represent?

$$CaCO_3(s) \rightarrow CaO(s) + CO_2(g)$$

1 mole of calcium carbonate would liberate 1 mole of carbon dioxide.
Choosing the appropriate units for the mole:
100 g of calcium carbonate would liberate 22.4 l of carbon dioxide at s.t.p.
50 g of calcium carbonate would liberate 11.2 l of carbon dioxide at s.t.p.
$\therefore$ 11.2 l will contain $3 \times 10^{23}$ molecules of carbon dioxide at s.t.p.

**Example 2** Calculate the charge required to liberate 0.56 litres of hydrogen at s.t.p. at the negative electrode (the cathode) in the electrolysis of dilute sulphuric acid. How many electrons does the charge represent?

$$H^+(aq) + 1e^- \rightarrow \tfrac{1}{2}H_2(g)$$

96 500 C     11.2 l at s.t.p.

4825 C will liberate 0.56 l at s.t.p.

4825 C represents $\frac{1}{20}$ of a mole of electrons $= \dfrac{6 \times 10^{23}}{20}$ electrons

$$= 3 \times 10^{22} \text{ electrons.}$$

**Example 3**   Calculate the mass in grams of a single atom of aluminium.

$6 \times 10^{23}$ atoms of aluminium have a mass of 27 g

1 atom of aluminium has a mass of $\dfrac{27}{6 \times 10^{23}}$ g $= 4.5 \times 10^{-23}$ g.

The kinetic theory of gases has led us to a new concept of the mole and this in turn allows us a whole range of concepts about the numbers of particles involved in chemical reactions.

### 3.10  X-ray analysis of sodium chloride

From a study of X-ray diffraction patterns produced by crystalline substances, it is possible to calculate the distances between centres of atoms in the crystal. In the case of sodium chloride the distance between the centre of a sodium ion and the centre of an adjacent chloride ion is $2.819 \times 10^{-8}$ cm. The density of sodium chloride is 2.165 g cm$^{-3}$, and the mass of a mole of sodium chloride is 58.443 g.

The volume of a crystal containing a mole of sodium chloride is

$\dfrac{58.443}{2.165}$ cm$^3$ = 26.99 cm$^3$

Because the crystal is cubic, the length of one edge of the crystal

$$= \sqrt[3]{26.995} \text{ cm} \approx \sqrt[3]{27.00} \text{ cm}^3$$

$$= 3.00 \text{ cm}$$

Number of ions in one edge of the crystal $= \dfrac{3.00}{2.819 \times 10^{-8}} = 1.064 \times 10^8$

Number of ions in the cube $= (1.064)^3 \times 10^{24} = 1.204 \times 10^{24}$

$$= 12.04 \times 10^{23}$$

Therefore, the crystal contains $6.02 \times 10^{23}$ sodium ions and $6.02 \times 10^{23}$ chloride ions.

**Summary**

From this chapter you should know:

1   Boyle's Law

2   Charles' Law and the Kelvin scale

3   the General Gas Equation and s.t.p. conditions

4   the Gas Constant for one mole leads to the molar volume

5   Faraday's Law

6   Avogadro's Law

7   Avogadro's Number

**Questions**

1   How many moles of copper(II) chloride are present in a solution which contains 13.45 g of the salt?
What is the maximum volume of chlorine at s.t.p. which could be obtained by electrolysis of this solution, assuming that all chloride ions present could be discharged as gas? *SCEEB*

2   'The fact that one volume of hydrogen combines with one volume of chlorine to form two volumes of hydrogen chloride can be shown with the following apparatus:

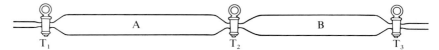

The limb A of the apparatus is filled with hydrogen. The limb B, which has half the volume of A, is filled with chlorine under atmospheric pressure. The gases are made to combine by opening the tap $T_2$ and placing the apparatus in diffuse daylight for several days. The tap $T_1$ is then opened under mercury. It is then closed and re-opened under water'.

Assume that hydrogen chloride is formed by the combination of equal volumes of hydrogen and chlorine as stated above.

1   What is the result of opening the tube under mercury?

2   What is the result of opening the tube under water?

3   If there is any gas remaining after opening under water what will it be, and how would you test for it?

4   Why was it necessary to open the tube under mercury *before* opening it under water?

5    What does the experiment tell you about the number of moles of chlorine that will combine with one mole of hydrogen?
What information is necessary to fix the molecular formula of hydrogen chloride, and how is it used for this purpose?
6    If A contains 224 cm$^3$ of hydrogen at s.t.p., how many moles of hydrogen chloride will be produced? *SCEEB*

3    Here are data concerning a small gas cylinder:

| | |
|---|---|
| Capacity | 100 cm$^3$ |
| Temperature | 0°C |
| Pressure of gas X inside cylinder | 4.0 atmosphere |
| Weight of cylinder when evacuated | 80.0 g |
| Weight of cylinder with gas X | 80.5 g |

Calculate the approximate molecular weight of the gas X. *SCEEB*

4    Copper(II) chloride solution is electrolysed until 1.0 g of copper is deposited at the cathode. If all the chlorine liberated at the anode were collected and measured at s.t.p. what would its volume be? *SCEEB*

5    $3CuO + 2NH_3 \rightarrow 3Cu + 3H_2O + N_2$

When 477 g of copper(II) oxide react with ammonia according to the above equation, calculate
1    the mass of copper produced
2    the volume of nitrogen produced at s.t.p. *SCEEB*

6    From the following data calculate the approximate molecular weight of the gas X.

Mass of plastic bottle empty = 112.80 g

Mass of plastic bottle + gas X = 113.52 g

Capacity of plastic bottle = 1 litre

*SCEEB*

7    How many molecules of fluorine are present in 19 g of fluorine gas? *SCEEB*

8    Oxygen can be converted into its polymorph, ozone, $O_3$, by electrical discharge, according to the equation.

$3O_2(g) \rightarrow 2O_3(g)$

If one mole of oxygen gas is completely converted into ozone, how many molecules of ozone would be produced? *SCEEB*

9    280 cm$^3$ of a gas were found to weigh 0.55 g at s.t.p. Calculate the molecular weight of the gas. *SCEEB*

10    Calculate the number of protons in 11.2 litres of oxygen gas at standard temperature and pressure.
(Take $N_A = 6 \times 10^{23}$). *P & W*

**11**   5.6 litres of oxygen combine with 8 g of sulphur at s.t.p.
   **1**   What is the formula of the oxide?
   **2**   Write the equation for the reaction of this oxide with water. *P & W*

**12**   A sample of potassium is 99.999 99% pure by weight. Assuming that the impurity is sodium, how many sodium atoms are present in 50 g of the sample? *P & W*

**13**   What volume will 1.7 g ammonia occupy at s.t.p.?
   How many atoms does this volume contain? *P & W*

**14**   How many coulombs of electricity are needed to produce 2.24 litres of hydrogen at s.t.p. from dilute sulphuric acid? *P & W*

**15**   During electrolysis of a solution of gold chloride, a current of 1.35 A flowing for 45 minutes deposited 2.5 g of gold. Calculate the number of units of charge on each of the gold ions, and hence write the formula for the chloride. *P & W*

**16**   13.0 g sodium azide when heated gave 4.6 g sodium and 6.72 l (measured at s.t.p.) of a gaseous element.
   What is the gaseous element?
   What is the empirical formula of sodium azide? *P & W*

**17**   0.332 g of a group II metal were deposited when a current of 0.5 A was passed for 88 minutes.
   Calculate the relative atomic mass of the metal and identify it. *P & W*

**18**   A tube, which had contained lighter fuel, was used in a molecular weight determination of an alkane.
   The results shown were obtained at s.t.p.

   Weight of tube + 300 cm$^3$ of gas  =  16.992 g

   Weight of tube  =  16.215 g

   Calculate the molecular weight of the gas and identify it. *P & W*

**19**   What is the maximum weight of gold which could be deposited by $6.02 \times 10^{22}$ electrons in the electrolysis of gold(III) chloride? *P & W*

# 4 Thermochemistry

## 4.1 Enthalpy

The energy stored in a compound is called the heat content or *enthalpy* of the compound. It is not possible to measure enthalpies directly, but it is possible to measure the energy change associated with a chemical reaction. This will represent the difference between the enthalpies of the reactants and products.

$$\Delta H \qquad = \Sigma H_p \quad - \quad \Sigma H_r$$

change in      enthalpy     enthalpy
enthalpy       of the       of the
              products    reactants

## 4.2 Exothermic and endothermic reactions

An **exothermic** reaction is one in which the enthalpy of the products is less than the enthalpy of the reactants, i.e. $\Delta H$ is negative.

$$CH_4(g) + 2O_2(g) \rightarrow CO_2(g) + 2H_2O(g) \qquad \Delta H = -892 \text{ kJ}$$

An **endothermic** reaction is one in which the enthalpy of the products is greater than the enthalpy of the reactants, i.e. $\Delta H$ is positive.

$$C(s) + 2S(s) \rightarrow CS_2(l) \qquad \Delta H = +107 \text{ kJ}$$

**Figure 4.1**    Change in enthalpy

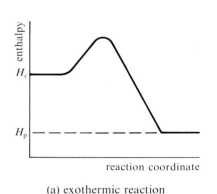

(a) exothermic reaction

(b) endothermic reaction

## 4.3 Hess's Law

We believe that energy cannot be created or destroyed. Bearing that in mind, let us consider the reaction

$$NaOH(s) + HCl(aq) \rightarrow NaCl(aq) + H_2O(l)$$

Aqueous sodium chloride can be prepared from solid sodium hydroxide in two different ways.

1  Dissolve the solid sodium hydroxide in water and produce aqueous sodium hydroxide. The enthalpy change is given by the value $\Delta H_1$.

$$Na^+OH^-(s) + H_2O(l) \rightarrow Na^+(aq) + OH^-(aq) \qquad \Delta H_1$$

2  Neutralize the aqueous sodium hydroxide with aqueous hydrochloric acid. The enthalpy change is given by the value $\Delta H_2$.

$$Na^+(aq) + OH^-(aq) + H^+(aq) + Cl^-(aq) \rightarrow Na^+(aq) + Cl^-(aq) + H_2O(l) \qquad \Delta H_2$$

3  Treat solid sodium hydroxide with aqueous hydrochloric acid until a neutral solution is obtained. The enthalpy change for the reaction is given by the value $\Delta H_3$.

$$Na^+OH^-(s) + H^+(aq) + Cl^-(aq) \rightarrow Na^+(aq) + Cl^-(aq) + H_2O(l) \qquad \Delta H_3.$$

By combining (1), (2) and (3) diagrammatically, we get:

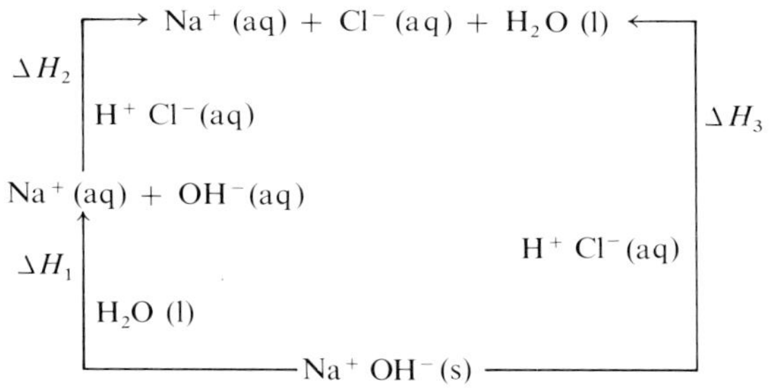

From the conservation of energy, we can see from the diagram that

$$\Delta H_3 = \Delta H_1 + \Delta H_2$$

The enthalpy change is the same irrespective of the path taken. This is **Hess's Law** which states that the heat change in a given reaction depends only upon the initial and final states of the system and is independent of the path followed. Hess's Law is of particular use in the calculation of enthalpy changes which cannot conveniently be determined in the laboratory.

**Example**    It is impossible to determine the enthalpy change for the reaction

$C(s) + \frac{1}{2}O_2(g) \rightarrow CO(g)$.

If we consider the following:

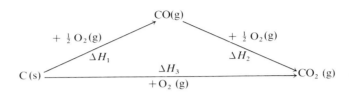

we can determine the enthalpy changes for:

$C(s) + O_2(g) \rightarrow CO_2(g)$          $\Delta H_3 = -394 \text{ kJ}$

$CO(g) + \frac{1}{2}O_2(g) \rightarrow CO_2(g)$          $\Delta H_2 = -284 \text{ kJ}$

From the diagram $\Delta H_3 = \Delta H_1 + \Delta H_2$

therefore                    $\Delta H_1 = \Delta H_3 - \Delta H_2$

$= -394 - (-284) \text{ kJ}$

$= -394 + 284$

$= -110 \text{ kJ}$

We get the enthalpy change for the reaction

$C(s) + \frac{1}{2}O_2(g) \rightarrow CO(g)$          $\Delta H = -110 \text{ kJ}$

A more formal approach is to set the calculation down as follows.
We know the enthalpy values for the following equations.

1                    $C(s) + O_2(g) \rightarrow CO_2(g)$                    $\Delta H = -394 \text{ kJ}$

2                    $CO(g) + \frac{1}{2}O_2(g) \rightarrow CO_2(g)$                    $\Delta H = -284 \text{ kJ}$

If we reverse equation 2 we get

3                    $CO_2(g) \rightarrow CO(g) + \frac{1}{2}O_2(g)$                    $\Delta H = +284 \text{ kJ}$

Now add equations 1 and 3.

$C(s) + O_2(g) \rightarrow CO_2(g)$                    $\Delta H = -394 \text{ kJ}$

$CO_2(g) \rightarrow CO(g) + \frac{1}{2}O_2(g)$                    $\Delta H = +284 \text{ kJ}$

$C(s) + O_2(g) + CO_2(g) \rightarrow CO_2(g) + CO(g) + \frac{1}{2}O_2(g)$    $\Delta H = -394 + 284$

Collecting the terms

$C(s) + \frac{1}{2}O_2(g) \rightarrow CO(g)$                    $\Delta H = -110 \text{ kJ}$

gives us the same result as before.

### 4.4 Enthalpy changes

Any reaction in which heat is evolved or absorbed involves enthalpy changes. Some examples of common enthalpy changes are given below, and more detailed thermochemical data is given in Table E on page 190.

**Ionization energy**
This is the energy required to remove one mole of electrons from a mole of atoms in the gaseous state, and thus produce a mole of positively charged ions.

$$K(g) \rightarrow K^+(g) + 1e^- \qquad \Delta H = +419 \text{ kJ}$$

**Electron affinity**
The electron affinity is the energy given out when a mole of neutral atoms combines with a mole of electrons to form a mole of negative ions in the gaseous state.

$$Cl(g) + 1e^- \rightarrow Cl^-(g) \qquad \Delta H = -356 \text{ kJ}$$

**Heat of vaporization**
This is the heat absorbed when one mole of a liquid at its boiling point is converted into a gas.

$$H_2O(l) \rightarrow H_2O(g) \qquad \Delta H = +41 \text{ kJ}$$

**Heat of sublimation**
This is the heat absorbed when one mole of a solid is converted into the gaseous state.

$$K(s) \rightarrow K(g) \qquad \Delta H = +90 \text{ kJ}$$

**Heat of fusion**
This is the heat absorbed by one mole of a solid when it is converted into the liquid state.

$$H_2O(s) \rightarrow H_2O(l) \qquad \Delta H = +6 \text{ kJ}$$

**Lattice energy**
This is the energy required to break all the bonds in one mole of an ionic crystal.

$$K^+Cl^-(s) \rightarrow K^+(g) + Cl^-(g) \qquad \Delta H = +760 \text{ kJ}$$

**Heat of solution**
This is the heat change when one mole of a substance is dissolved in such an amount of water that any further dilution results in no detectable heat change.

**Example**
When 10.6 g of sodium carbonate are dissolved in 100 cm³ of water, the following results are obtained:

$$\text{mass of water} = 100 \text{ g}$$
$$\text{initial temperature of water} = 20 \,°C \qquad (T_1)$$
$$\text{final temperature of water} = 25 \,°C \qquad (T_2)$$
$$\text{temperature change } \Delta T = T_2 - T_1$$
$$= 25 - 20 = 5 \text{ C}°$$

The enthalpy change for the reaction can be calculated from the equation

$$\Delta H = cm\Delta T$$

where  $c$ = specific heat capacity of water and is 4.2 J g$^{-1}$ K$^{-1}$

$m$ = mass in grams

$\Delta T$ = temperature change

Substituting the values

$$\Delta H = 4.2 \times 100 \times 5 = 2100 \text{ J}$$

This is the enthalpy change for the solution of 0.1 moles of sodium carbonate; therefore for 1 mole, $\Delta H = 21\,000 \text{ J} = 21 \text{ kJ}$

i.e.   $Na_2CO_3(s) + H_2O(l) \rightarrow Na_2CO_3(aq)$      $\Delta H = -21 \text{ kJ}$

**Heat of neutralization**   This is the amount of heat evolved when one mole of water is formed by the neutralization of an acid with a base.

$$H^+Cl^-(aq) + Na^+OH^-(aq) \rightarrow Na^+Cl^-(aq) + H_2O(l)$$

or      $H^+(aq) + OH^-(aq) \rightarrow H_2O(l)$

Any acid-base reaction can be represented by the reaction between the hydrogen and hydroxide ions to form water.

**Example**   Consider the reaction between 100 cm³ of 1M HCl and 100 cm³ of 1M NaOH. The acid and alkali are placed in separate vacuum flasks and the temperature of each solution is noted. The alkali is added to the acid and the highest temperature reached is recorded.

Temperature of acid $= 20 \,°C$

Temperature of alkali $= 20 \,°C$

Temperature after mixing $= 26.5 \,°C$

Rise in temperature $\Delta T = 26.5 - 20 = 6.5 \,C°$

$$\Delta H = cm\Delta T$$

$$= 4.2 \times 200 \times 6.5 = 5460 \text{ J}.$$

This is the enthalpy change for the formation of 0.1 mole of water. Since we began with 0.1 moles of acid and alkali, the heat changed for 1 mole would be 54 600 or 54.6 kJ

$H^+(aq) + OH^-(aq) \rightarrow H_2O(l)$      $\Delta H = -54.6 \text{ kJ}$

**Heat of formation**   The heat of formation is the heat change when one mole of a compound is formed from its elements in their normal states.

$C(s) + 2H_2(g) \rightarrow CH_4(g)$      $\Delta H = -75 \text{ kJ}$

When one mole of methane is formed from solid carbon and gaseous hydrogen at 25 °C (298 K) and one atmosphere pressure, then 75 kJ are produced.

**Heat of combustion**   The heat of combustion is the amount of heat produced when one mole of a compound is completely burned in oxygen. As we might expect, all $\Delta H$ values for heats of combustion are negative.

$CH_4(g) + 2O_2(g) \rightarrow CO_2(g) + 2H_2O(g)$      $\Delta H = -892 \text{ kJ}$

## 4.5  Bond energies

One principal use of enthalpy changes, especially heats of combustion and heats of formation, is in the calculation of bond energies.

$$H_2(g) \rightarrow 2H(g) \qquad \Delta H = +437 \text{ kJ}$$

Bond energies can in turn be used to predict the enthalpy change of another reaction. Two examples of the determination of bond energy from experimental data are given below.

The energy of a bond is always calculated on the basis that the reactants are gaseous atoms. Thus the heat of formation of methane is given by

$$C(s) + 2H_2(g) \rightarrow CH_4(g) \qquad \Delta H = -75 \text{ kJ}$$

but the bond formation energy of the C—H bond is in fact one quarter of the enthalpy change of the following reaction (where the reactants are all gaseous):

$$C(g) + 4H(g) \rightarrow CH_4(g) \qquad \Delta H = ?$$

**Determination of the C—H bond dissociation energy**

We shall need the following information from data tables or from experimental data concerning enthalpy changes:

① Heat of sublimation of carbon $\qquad C(s) \rightarrow C(g) \qquad \Delta H = +715 \text{ kJ}$

② Heat of dissociation of hydrogen $\qquad H_2(g) \rightarrow 2H(g) \qquad \Delta H = +437 \text{ kJ}$

③ Heat of formation of methane $\qquad C(s) + 2H_2(g) \rightarrow CH_4(g) \qquad \Delta H = -75 \text{ kJ}$

By using these equations and Hess's law correctly, we can obtain the enthalpy changes for the equation:

$$C(g) + 2H_2(g) \rightarrow CH_4(g).$$

Reverse ①: $\qquad C(g) \rightarrow C(s) \qquad \Delta H = -715 \text{ kJ}$

Reverse ②, then ×2: $\qquad 4H(g) \rightarrow 2H_2(g) \qquad \Delta H = -874 \text{ kJ}$

Include ③: $\qquad C(s) + 2H_2(g) \rightarrow CH_4(g) \qquad \Delta H = -75 \text{ kJ}$

Then add: $\qquad C(g) + 4H(g) + C(s) + 2H_2(g) \rightarrow C(s) + 2H_2(g) + CH_4(g) \qquad \Delta H = -1664 \text{ kJ}$

and collect terms: $\qquad C(g) + 4H(g) \rightarrow CH_4(g) \qquad \Delta H = -1664 \text{ kJ}$

Thus the bond energy associated with the formation of four C—H bonds is $-1664$ kJ.

i.e. bond formation energy of C—H $\quad = -416$ kJ
bond dissociation energy of C—H $\quad = +416$ kJ

The figure quoted in data tables is the mean bond dissociation energy averaged over a large number of compounds.

**Determination of the C—C bond dissociation energy**

We know from above that the C—H bond energy is $+416$ kJ. We can therefore calculate the C—C bond energy in ethane if we can determine the enthalpy change for

$$2C(g) + 6H(g) \rightarrow C_2H_6(g)$$

We require the following information:

① Heat of sublimation of carbon $\quad\quad\quad$ $C(s) \rightarrow C(g)$ $\quad\quad\quad\quad\quad\quad\quad\quad$ $\Delta H = +715$ kJ

② Heat of dissociation of hydrogen $\quad\quad$ $H_2(g) \rightarrow 2H(g)$ $\quad\quad\quad\quad\quad\quad$ $\Delta H = +437$ kJ

③ Heat of formation of ethane $\quad\quad$ $2C(s) + 3H_2(g) \rightarrow C_2H_6(g)$ $\quad\quad$ $\Delta H = -85$ kJ

Reverse ①, then $\times 2$: $\quad\quad\quad\quad\quad\quad$ $2C(g) \rightarrow 2C(s)$ $\quad\quad\quad\quad\quad\quad\quad\quad$ $\Delta H = -1430$ kJ

Reverse ②, then $\times 3$: $\quad\quad\quad\quad\quad\quad$ $6H(g) \rightarrow 3H_2(g)$ $\quad\quad\quad\quad\quad\quad\quad$ $\Delta H = -1311$ kJ

Include ③: $\quad\quad\quad\quad\quad\quad\quad$ $2C(s) + 3H_2(g) \rightarrow C_2H_6(g)$ $\quad\quad$ $\Delta H = -85$ kJ

Then add: $\quad\quad$ $2C(g) + 6H(g) + \cancel{3H_2(g)} + \cancel{2C(s)} \rightarrow \cancel{2C(s)} + \cancel{3H_2(g)} + C_2H_6(g)$ $\quad$ $\Delta H = -2826$ kJ

and collect terms: $\quad\quad\quad\quad\quad\quad$ $2C(g) + 6H(g) \rightarrow C_2H_6(g)$ $\quad\quad\quad\quad$ $\Delta H = -2826$ kJ

The total bond dissociation energies are $+2826$ kJ.

Therefore the C—C bond dissociation energy in ethane

$$= +2826 - (6 \times \text{C—H bond energy from first example})$$

$$= +2826 - (6 \times 416)$$

$$= +2826 - 2496$$

$$= +330 \text{ kJ.}$$

The bond dissociation energy in C—C is $+330$ kJ mol$^{-1}$.

### 4.6 Calculations involving enthalpy changes

**Example 1** $\quad$ Calculate the heat of formation of methane, given that the heats of combustion of hydrogen, carbon and methane are 286, 406 and 888 kJ mol$^{-1}$ respectively.

Write down the equation for which the enthalpy change is required.

$$C(s) + 2H_2(g) \rightarrow CH_4(g)$$

Write down the information given in equation form

①  $\quad\quad\quad\quad\quad\quad\quad$ $H_2(g) + \tfrac{1}{2}O_2(g) \rightarrow H_2O(g)$ $\quad\quad\quad$ $\Delta H = -286$ kJ

②  $\quad\quad\quad\quad\quad\quad\quad\quad$ $C(s) + O_2(g) \rightarrow CO_2(g)$ $\quad\quad\quad\quad$ $\Delta H = -406$ kJ

③  $\quad\quad\quad\quad\quad$ $CH_4(g) + 2O_2(g) \rightarrow CO_2(g) + 2H_2O(g)$ $\quad$ $\Delta H = -888$ kJ

Multiply ① by 2 $\quad\quad\quad\quad$ $2H_2(g) + O_2(g) \rightarrow 2H_2O(g)$ $\quad\quad\quad$ $\Delta H = -572$ kJ

Leave ② $\quad\quad\quad\quad\quad\quad\quad$ $C(s) + O_2(g) \rightarrow CO_2(g)$ $\quad\quad\quad\quad$ $\Delta H = -406$ kJ

Reverse ③ $\quad\quad\quad\quad$ $CO_2(g) + 2H_2O(g) \rightarrow CH_4(g) + 2O_2(g)$ $\quad$ $\Delta H = +888$ kJ

Add $\quad$ $C(s) + 2H_2(g) + 2O_2(g) + CO_2(g) + 2H_2O(g) \rightarrow CH_4(g) + 2O_2(g) + CO_2(g) + 2H_2O(g)$

$$\Delta H = -572 - 406 + 888 \text{ kJ}$$

Collect the terms $\quad\quad\quad\quad$ $C(s) + 2H_2(g) \rightarrow CH_4(g)$ $\quad\quad\quad\quad$ $\Delta H = -90$ kJ

The heat of formation of methane is $-90$ kJ mol$^{-1}$

**Example 2**   Calculate the heat of formation of ethane, given that the heats of combustion of carbon, hydrogen and ethane are 394, 286 and 1560 kJ mol$^{-1}$ respectively.

Write down the equation required

$$2C(s) + 3H_2(g) \rightarrow C_2H_6(g)$$

Write down the given information in equation form

①            $C(s) + O_2(g) \rightarrow CO_2(g)$            $\Delta H = -394 \text{ kJ}$

②            $H_2(g) + \frac{1}{2}O_2(g) \rightarrow H_2O(g)$            $\Delta H = -286 \text{ kJ}$

③            $C_2H_6(g) + \frac{7}{2}O_2(g) \rightarrow 2CO_2(g) + 3H_2O(g)$            $\Delta H = -1560 \text{ kJ}$

Multiply ① by 2            $2C(s) + 2O_2(g) \rightarrow 2CO_2(g)$            $\Delta H = -788 \text{ kJ}$

Multiply ② by 3            $3H_2(g) + \frac{3}{2}O_2(g) \rightarrow 3H_2O(g)$            $\Delta H = -858 \text{ kJ}$

Reverse ③            $2CO_2(g) + 3H_2O(g) \rightarrow C_2H_6(g) + \frac{7}{2}O_2(g)$            $\Delta H = +1560 \text{ kJ}$

Add        $2C(s) + 3H_2(g) + \frac{7}{2}O_2(g) + 2CO_2(g) + 3H_2O(g) \rightarrow C_2H_6(g) + \frac{7}{2}O_2(g) + 2CO_2(g) + 3H_2O(g)$

$$\Delta H = -86 \text{ kJ}$$

Collect the terms            $2C(s) + 3H_2(g) \rightarrow C_2H_6(g)$            $\Delta H = -86 \text{ kJ}$

The heat of formation of ethane is $-86 \text{ kJ mol}^{-1}$

**Summary**

From this chapter you should know:

1   Enthalpy is the heat content of a substance.

2   For exothermic reactions, $\Delta H$ is negative; for endothermic reactions, $\Delta H$ is positive.

3   Hess's Law and its applications.

4   Bond-breaking is endothermic and bond-making is exothermic.

5   How bond dissociation energies are obtained.

**Questions**

1    Given that         $H_2(g) \rightarrow 2H(g)$;                    $\Delta H = +435$ kJ

$Br_2(g) \rightarrow 2Br(g)$;                    $\Delta H = +192$ kJ

$2HBr(g) \rightarrow 2H(g) + 2Br(g)$;        $\Delta H = +728$ kJ

calculate from these data
1    the energy of the H—Br bond,
2    the heat of formation of hydrogen bromide from the gaseous elements.
*SCEEB*

2    The table below shows the heat of neutralization for some acid/base reactions.

| Acid | Base | Heat of neutralization $-\Delta H$ kJ mol$^{-1}$ |
|------|------|--------------------------------------------------|
| HCl | NaOH | 57.3 |
| HCl | $NH_3$ | 52.2 |
| X | KOH | 55.2 |
| HCl | Y | 53.4 |
| $HNO_3$ | Z | 57.3 |

From the following list

KOH   HCl   $NH_3$   $CH_3COOH$   $C_2H_5OH$   $HNO_3$   $C_2H_5NH_2$

choose a suitable substance to represent X; Y; Z. *SCEEB*

3    The reaction between hydrogen and chlorine is thought to involve the following stages:

$Cl_2(g) \rightarrow 2Cl\cdot(g)$                    (A)

$Cl\cdot(g) + H_2(g) \rightarrow HCl(g) + H\cdot(g)$        (B)

$H\cdot(g) + Cl_2(g) \rightarrow HCl(g) + Cl\cdot(g)$        (C)

1    Use the Mean Bond Dissociation Energies listed on page 190 in this book to calculate the Heat of Reaction for each of the processes (A), (B), and (C). Indicate by + or − sign which are endothermic and which exothermic.
2    Use the results obtained in 1 to predict which of these stages is likely to be the rate-determining step in the reaction between hydrogen and chlorine. *SCEEB*

4    The energy level diagram below shows the enthalpy changes associated with the formation of solid potassium chloride from its elements in their standard states. Upward arrows indicate endothermic processes and downward arrows indicate exothermic processes.
$\Delta H_1$, the Heat of Formation of potassium chloride, is the net result of all the other enthalpy changes.

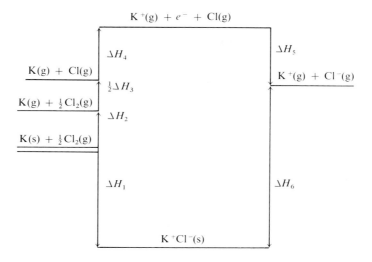

1    $\Delta H_1$ is the Heat of Formation of solid potassium chloride and $\Delta H_6$ is the Lattice Energy of potassium chloride. What names are given to the enthalpy changes $\Delta H_2$, $\Delta H_3$, $\Delta H_4$, and $\Delta H_5$?

2    Given that    $\Delta H_1 = -436 \text{ kJ mol}^{-1}$

$$\Delta H_2 = +90 \text{ kJ mol}^{-1}$$

$$\Delta H_5 = -356 \text{ kJ mol}^{-1}$$

make use of the data on pages 186 and 190 in this book to calculate the Lattice Energy of KCl(s). *SCEEB*

5

| Bond | Bond energy kJ mol$^{-1}$ |
|------|------|
| N—H | 391 |
| N≡N | 941 |
| H—H | 435 |

Use the values of bond energy given in the table to calculate the Heat of Formation of 1 mole of ammonia from its elements. Show all your working and indicate clearly whether the reaction is exothermic or endothermic. *SCEEB*

6    The heat of formation of aluminium oxide is $-1596 \times 10^3 \text{ J mol}^{-1}$ and that for chromium oxide is $-1134 \times 10^3 \text{ J mol}^{-1}$. Calculate the heat of reaction for:

$$2Al + Cr_2O_3 \rightarrow Al_2O_3 + 2Cr. \quad P \& W$$

7
$$\Delta H \text{ kJ}$$

$$O_2(g) \rightarrow 2O(g) \qquad +496$$

$$C(s) \rightarrow C(g) \qquad +715$$

$$C(s) + O_2(g) \rightarrow CO_2(g) \qquad -394$$

Calculate
1    $\Delta H$ for the reaction $C(g) + 2O(g) \rightarrow CO_2(g)$
2    the energy of the carbon to oxygen bond in carbon dioxide. *P & W*

8    Explain how the following information can be used to verify Hess's Law.

$$\Delta H \text{ kJ}$$

$$NH_3(g) + HCl(g) \rightarrow NH_4^+Cl^-(s) \qquad -176$$

$$NH_3(aq) + HCl(aq) \rightarrow NH_4^+(aq) + Cl^-(aq) \qquad -51.5$$

$$NH_3(g) + aq \rightarrow NH_3(aq) \qquad -35.2$$

$$HCl(g) + aq \rightarrow HCl(aq) \qquad -72.5$$

$$NH_4^+Cl^-(s) + aq \rightarrow NH_4^+(aq) + Cl^-(aq) \qquad +16.8$$

*P & W*

9    $CO(g) + \frac{1}{2}O_2(g) \rightarrow CO_2(g) \qquad \Delta H = -283 \text{ kJ}$

$Cu(s) + \frac{1}{2}O_2(g) \rightarrow CuO(s) \qquad \Delta H = -155 \text{ kJ}$

Write a balanced equation to show the reduction of copper(II) oxide by carbon monoxide and calculate the heat of this reaction. *P & W*

10    When 2 g of sulphur were completely burned in air, the heat evolved raised the temperature of 222 g of water from 18 °C to 38 °C. Calculate the heat of combustion of sulphur. *P & W*

11    The heats of combustion of propanol, carbon and hydrogen are $-2010$, $-394$ and $-286$ kJ mol$^{-1}$.
Calculate the heat of formation of propanol. *P & W*

# 5 Oxidation and reduction

### 5.1 Oxidation

At one time the name **oxidation** was given to any chemical reaction in which a substance combined with oxygen.

**Example 1** When oxygen gas is passed over heated copper, the copper combines with the oxygen to form copper(II) oxide. In other words the copper is oxidized.

$$2Cu(s) + O_2(g) \rightarrow 2CuO(s)$$

What does the oxidation of copper mean in terms of electron transfer?

$$2Cu(s) \rightarrow 2Cu^{2+}(s) + 4e^-$$

The copper metal has lost electrons, and in doing so, it has formed copper(II) ions.

**Example 2** When magnesium burns in oxygen, the magnesium combines with the oxygen to form magnesium oxide. In other words the magnesium is oxidized.

$$2Mg(s) + O_2(g) \rightarrow 2MgO(s)$$

What does the oxidation of magnesium mean in terms of electron transfer?

$$2Mg(s) \rightarrow 2Mg^{2+}(s) + 4e^-$$

The magnesium metal has lost electrons, and in doing so, it has formed magnesium ions.

The two examples would indicate that oxidation is a loss of electrons. All reactions concerning the gain of oxygen involve a loss of electrons. Oxidation, therefore, can be extended to include any reaction which involves a loss of electrons. **Oxidation** is now defined as a **loss of electrons**.

**Example 3** Magnesium reacts with dilute hydrochloric acid to form magnesium chloride and hydrogen gas.

$$Mg(s) + 2HCl(aq) \rightarrow MgCl_2(aq) + H_2(g)$$

The magnesium is losing electrons to form magnesium ions.

$$Mg(s) \rightarrow Mg^{2+}(aq) + 2e^-$$

The magnesium is being oxidized.

### 5.2 Reduction

At one time the name **reduction** was given to any chemical reaction in which oxygen was removed from a substance.

**Example 1**    When hydrogen gas is passed over heated copper(II) oxide, the hydrogen removes the oxygen. In other words the copper(II) oxide is reduced.

$$CuO(s) + H_2(g) \rightarrow Cu(s) + H_2O(l)$$

What does the reduction of copper(II) oxide mean in terms of electron transfer?

$$Cu^{2+} + 2e^- \rightarrow Cu(s)$$

The copper(II) ion has gained electrons and in doing so has formed copper metal.

**Example 2**    When silver(I) oxide is heated, silver metal and oxygen gas are produced. The silver(I) oxide is reduced.

$$2Ag_2O(s) \rightarrow 4Ag(s) + O_2(g)$$

What does the reduction of silver(I) oxide mean in terms of electron transfer?

$$4Ag^+(s) + 4e^- \rightarrow 4Ag(s)$$

The silver(I) ion has gained electrons and in doing so has formed silver metal.

The two examples considered would indicate that reduction is a gain of electrons. All reactions concerning the loss of oxygen involve a gain of electrons. Reduction, therefore, can be extended to include any reaction which involves a gain of electrons. **Reduction** is now defined as a **gain of electrons**.

**Example 3**    Iron(III) oxide reacts with carbon monoxide gas to form iron metal and carbon dioxide gas.

$$Fe_2O_3(s) + 3CO(g) \rightarrow 2Fe(s) + 3CO_2(g)$$

The iron(III) ions are gaining electrons to form iron metal.

$$2Fe^{3+} + 6e^- \rightarrow 2Fe(s)$$

The iron(III) ion is being reduced.


## 5.3 Redox

Oxidation and reduction always occur at the same time in a chemical reaction. Every time a loss of electrons takes place in part of the reaction, there is an equivalent gain of electrons in another part of the reaction. Let us consider again the reaction between heated copper and oxygen. The oxidation process is:

$$Cu(s) \rightarrow Cu^{2+}(s) + 2e^-$$

The reduction process is:

$$O_2(g) + 4e^- \rightarrow 2O^{2-}(s)$$

If we adjust the equations so that the number of electrons lost is equal to the number of electrons gained, and add the two equations, we obtain the overall equation in terms of the reacting species.

Reduction        $O_2(g) + 4e^- \rightarrow 2O^{2-}(s)$

Oxidation        $2Cu(s) \rightarrow 2Cu^{2+}(s) + 4e^-$

Redox        $2Cu(s) + O_2(g) \rightarrow (2Cu^{2+} + 2O^{2-})(s)$

This is called the **redox equation**.

A redox equation can be constructed in a similar way for the reaction of heat on silver(I) oxide. The oxidation process is:

$2O^{2-}(s) \rightarrow O_2(g) + 4e^-$

The reduction process is

$Ag^+(s) + 1e^- \rightarrow Ag(s)$

The equations are adjusted to ensure that the number of electrons lost is the same as the number of electrons gained and the redox equation is then obtained.

Reduction        $4Ag^+(s) + 4e^- \rightarrow 4Ag(s)$

Oxidation        $2O^{2-}(s) \rightarrow O_2(g) + 4e^-$

Redox        $(4Ag^+ + 2O^{2-})(s) \rightarrow 4Ag(s) + O_2(g)$

In these two examples the redox equation is more or less the same as the overall equation, but this is not always the case.

**Example**    When yellow iron(III) chloride solution is mixed with sodium sulphite solution, the solution changes to a pale green colour. Can we account for this in terms of redox? The colour change is due to the reduction of the yellow iron(III) ion to the green iron(II) ion.

$Fe^{3+}(aq) + 1e^- \rightarrow Fe^{2+}(aq)$

The corresponding oxidation step is the oxidation of the sulphite ion to the sulphate ion.

$SO_3^{2-}(aq) \rightarrow SO_4^{2-}(aq)$

This equation is not balanced but balancing it can be done in three steps.

1    Add sufficient water molecules to balance the number of oxygen atoms.

$SO_3^{2-}(aq) + H_2O(l) \rightarrow SO_4^{2-}(aq)$

2    Add sufficient hydrogen ions to balance the hydrogen in the water molecules.

$SO_3^{2-}(aq) + H_2O(l) \rightarrow SO_4^{2-}(aq) + 2H^+(aq)$

3    Add the correct number of electrons to make each side electrically equivalent.

$SO_3^{2-}(aq) + H_2O(l) \rightarrow SO_4^{2-}(aq) + 2H^+(aq) + 2e^-$

We now have the oxidation and reduction reactions.

$$Fe^{3+}(aq) + 1e^- \rightarrow Fe^{2+}(aq)$$

$$SO_3^{2-}(aq) + H_2O(l) \rightarrow SO_4^{2-}(aq) + 2H^+(aq) + 2e^-$$

The equations are now adjusted so that the number of electrons lost is equal to the number of electrons gained.

Reduction

$$2Fe^{3+}(aq) + 2e^- \rightarrow 2Fe^{2+}(aq)$$

Oxidation

$$SO_3^{2-}(aq) + H_2O(l) \rightarrow SO_4^{2-}(aq) + 2H^+(aq) + 2e^-$$

Redox

$$2Fe^{3+}(aq) + SO_3^{2-}(aq) + H_2O(l) \rightarrow 2Fe^{2+}(aq) + SO_4^{2-}(aq) + 2H^+(aq)$$

If we write the equation for the reaction between iron(III) chloride and sodium sulphite solution we obtain the following:

$$2FeCl_3(aq) + Na_2SO_3(aq) + H_2O(l) \rightarrow 2FeCl_2(aq) + Na_2SO_4(aq) + 2HCl(aq)$$

$$2Fe^{3+}(aq) + 6Cl^-(aq) + 2Na^+(aq) \atop + SO_3^{2-}(aq) + H_2O(l) \rightarrow {2Fe^{2+}(aq) + 6Cl^-(aq) + 2Na^+(aq) \atop + SO_4^{2-}(aq) + 2H^+(aq)}$$

If we compare the redox equation and the complete equation we can see one significant difference. There are no sodium or chloride ions in the redox equation. These ions are unchanged during the reaction, and take no part in the reaction. These ions are called **spectator** ions. The redox equation shows how the reaction proceeds in terms of the reacting species only. We can show by using chemical tests that

$$Fe^{3+}(aq) \rightarrow Fe^{2+}(aq) \qquad \text{and} \qquad SO_3^{2-}(aq) \rightarrow SO_4^{2-}(aq)$$

**Test for iron(II)/ iron(III)**   Iron(III) turns ammonium thiocyanate solution dark red. Iron(II) does not turn ammonium thiocyanate solution red. Iron(II) gives a 'Prussian blue' precipitate with potassium hexacyanoferrate(III) solution.

**Test for sulphite/ sulphate**   A sulphite, when added to barium chloride solution, forms a white precipitate of barium sulphite, which is soluble in dilute hydrochloric acid. A sulphate, when added to barium chloride solution, forms a white precipitate of barium sulphate, which is insoluble in dilute hydrochloric acid.

## 5.4 Oxidizing and reducing agents

When zinc is dropped into copper(II) sulphate solution, the zinc displaces copper from the solution. The zinc is oxidized and the copper is reduced. **Oxidizing agents** are substances which accept electrons. In this case the copper ions are accepting electrons when the zinc is oxidized. **Reducing agents** are substances which donate electrons. In this case the zinc atoms are donating electrons when the copper(II) ion is reduced.

Reduction

$$Cu^{2+}(aq) + 2e^- \rightarrow Cu(s)$$

Oxidation

$$Zn(s) \rightarrow Zn^{2+}(aq) + 2e^-$$

Redox

$$Zn(s) + Cu^{2+}(aq) \rightarrow Zn^{2+}(aq) + Cu(s)$$

The oxidizing agent is $Cu^{2+}(aq)$.
The reducing agent is $Zn(s)$.

### 5.5 Voltaic cells

A redox reaction involves a transfer of electrons. We can demonstrate this by using the apparatus shown in Figure 5.1.

**Figure 5.1** A voltaic cell

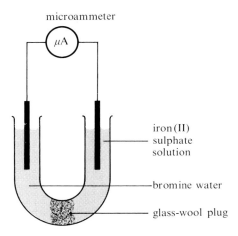

microammeter

μA

iron (II) sulphate solution

bromine water

glass-wool plug

Almost immediately, the microammeter shows a current, indicating a flow of electrons. A transfer of electrons must be occurring. We can show this by means of visual observations and chemical tests.

The bromine water is a red-brown colour to begin with, due to the presence of molecular bromine $Br_2$. As the experiment progresses the colour gets lighter and lighter until the solution becomes colourless. It is known that the bromide ion is colourless. Therefore, the bromine has been reduced to form bromide ions.

$Br_2(aq) + 2e^- \rightarrow 2Br^-(aq)$
red-brown              colourless

We already know how to distinguish between iron(II) and iron(III) ions (section 5.3). If the iron(II) solution is tested with ammonium thiocyanate solution about fifteen minutes after setting up the experiment, a dark red colour is produced. Iron(III) ions have been formed. The iron(II) has been oxidized to iron(III).

$Fe^{2+}(aq) \rightarrow Fe^{3+}(aq) + 1e^-$

We can now construct the redox equation:

| | |
|---|---|
| Reduction | $Br_2(aq) + 2e^- \rightarrow 2Br^-(aq)$ |
| Oxidation | $2Fe^{2+}(aq) \rightarrow 2Fe^{3+}(aq) + 2e^-$ |
| Redox | $2Fe^{2+}(aq) + Br_2(aq) \rightarrow 2Fe^{3+}(aq) + 2Br^-(aq)$ |

From the meter reading we know there is a transfer of electrons and we have shown that oxidation and reduction (redox) have occurred.

We get similar reactions when chlorine water is used in place of bromine water. However, iron(II) ions cannot reduce iodine to iodide. In this case iron(III) ions oxidize iodide ions to iodine, since iodide ions are stronger reducing agents than iron(II) ions.

**Test for chlorine/ chloride**    Chlorine water is yellow-green in colour. Chloride ions in solution are colourless. Chloride ions give a white precipitate of silver(I) chloride with silver(I) nitrate solution.

**Test for iodine/ iodide**    Iodine in water gives a brown colour. Iodide ions in solution are colourless. Iodide ions give a yellow precipitate of silver(I) iodide with silver(I) nitrate solution.

Figure 5.1 is an example of a voltaic cell. Essentially, a voltaic cell consists of two electrodes combined in such a way that, when they are connected by a conductor, an electric current will be produced (Figure 5.2).

**Figure 5.2**

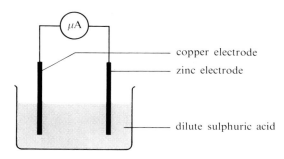

Zinc is higher in the reactivity series than copper and electrons will flow from the zinc to the copper. The zinc strip is being oxidized.

$$Zn(s) \rightarrow Zn^{2+}(aq) + 2e^-$$

We call the electrode at which oxidation occurs the **anode**. The electrons arriving at the copper electrode will not affect the copper, but they will combine with hydrogen ions from the sulphuric acid to form hydrogen gas:

$$2H^+(aq) + 2e^- \rightarrow H_2(g)$$

The hydrogen ion is being reduced and we call the electrode at which reduction occurs the **cathode**.

### 5.6  Electrode potentials

If the ammeter in Figure 5.2 is replaced by a voltmeter, the reading will be nearly 1.10 volts. This value depends on the abilities of the metals zinc and copper to form ions in the solution. To obtain some order of ability to form ions it seems appropriate to measure the voltage for a large number of cells in which one electrode is held constant as a standard.

**Figure 5.3**

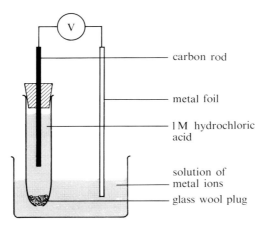

carbon rod

metal foil

1 M hydrochloric acid

solution of metal ions

glass wool plug

Some typical results are shown in Table 5.1.

**Table 5.1** Electrode potentials against a carbon standard

| Metal | Voltage (V) |
|---|---|
| magnesium | 2.8 |
| aluminium | 2.0 |
| zinc | 1.2 |
| iron | 0.9 |
| tin | 0.5 |
| lead | 0.4 |
| copper | 0.1 |

While the standard electrode shown here is convenient for the school laboratory, the values for electrode potentials given in data books are measured against a hydrogen electrode under standard conditions.

The hydrogen electrode (Figure 5.4) is used as a standard reference electrode, and all values of electrode potential are determined using hydrogen, which is given an arbitrary value of zero. Table 5.2 shows some standard values that have been determined in this way.

**Table 5.2** Electrode potentials using standard $H_2$ reference electrode

| Metal | Electrode potential (V) | Metal | Electrode potential (V) |
|---|---|---|---|
| Potassium | −2.92 | Tin | −0.15 |
| Calcium | −2.87 | Lead | −0.13 |
| Sodium | −2.71 | Hydrogen | 0.00 |
| Magnesium | −2.34 | Copper | +0.34 |
| Aluminium | −1.71 | Silver | +0.80 |
| Zinc | −0.76 | Mercury | +0.85 |
| Iron | −0.44 | Gold | +1.68 |

**Figure 5.4** The hydrogen electrode

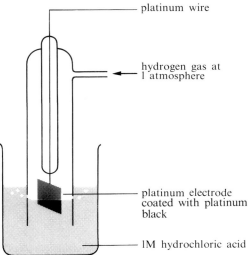

platinum wire

hydrogen gas at 1 atmosphere

platinum electrode coated with platinum black

1M hydrochloric acid

You will see from Table 5.2 that hydrogen is given the value of 0.00 V. This standard value is assigned arbitrarily. The sign for the other values is given by the sign of the charge produced by the electrode relative to the hydrogen electrode. The most significant point which emerges from Table 5.2 is that it confirms the reactivity series. It gives us a measure of the readiness of a metal to form ions. If a metal has a high negative electrode potential, it will be very reactive. If it has a high positive electrode potential, it will be unreactive.

To this point in the text we have used the concept of electrode potential to support the reactivity series for metals, but it is possible to extend this concept to deal with the relative strengths of oxidizing agents and reducing agents other than metals. For example, let us consider the cell in Figure 5.5.

**Figure 5.5**

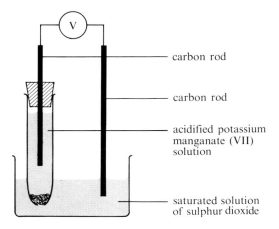

carbon rod

carbon rod

acidified potassium manganate (VII) solution

saturated solution of sulphur dioxide

A flow of electrons in the external circuit indicates that there is a redox reaction possible between the two solutions. From our laboratory experience, we know that sulphur dioxide decolorizes acidified potassium manganate(VII). By setting up a cell as shown in Figure 5.5, we can measure the voltage difference between the two half-cells, and this is a measure of the possibility of the reaction taking place at standard conditions. This method gives us a means of comparing the relative strengths of oxidizing agents and reducing agents: this is explained in more detail in examples 1 and 2 below.

The electrode potential measured in this way under standard conditions (itemized below) against a standard hydrogen electrode is termed the **standard reduction electrode potential** $E°$: a list of these is given in Data table D in this book, page 189. By convention, the half-cell reactions are all written as reduction reactions. Consequently, the negative sign implies that the reaction is more likely to go in the opposite direction under standard conditions, that is as an oxidation.

### Notes on standard conditions

1  The temperature is 298 K (25 °C).
2  Gases are at 1 atmosphere pressure.
3  Solutions are molar. For example, zinc would be in contact with 1M $Zn^{2+}(aq)$ solution.

We can use $E°$ values in several ways.

**Determination of the e.m.f. of a cell**

**Figure 5.6**

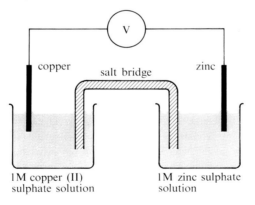

From the table of standard reduction electrode potentials (Data table D), we can use the list of $E°$ values as if it were a scale.

$E°$ for $Zn^{2+}(aq) = -0.76$ V

$E°$ for $Cu^{2+}(aq) = +0.34$ V

The difference between these two electrode potentials is $-1.10$ V or $+1.10$ V, and this corresponds to the reading on the voltmeter. However, we shall see shortly the significance of the sign which determines the direction in which the electrons flow.

The cells illustrated in Figures 5.5 and 5.6 are used in experiments to determine the voltage. They have a very high internal resistance and consequently they would not deliver sufficient current to allow their use as working cells. If we had to light a bulb for instance, we could use this redox system to make a simple working cell as shown in Figure 5.7.

**Figure 5.7**

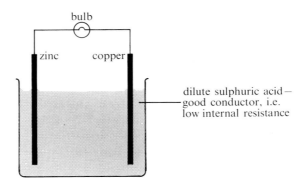

**Predicting the possibility of a reaction**

If we write down the half-reactions for the oxidation and reduction processes at the electrodes and **add** them together to give the overall redox equation, the value of $E$ will be positive if the equation represents the correct reaction. If $E$ is negative, the reaction is written in the reverse direction. In this way we are able to predict whether the redox reaction will take place **under standard conditions**.

From earlier work on the reactivity series, we might expect the electrons in the cell shown in Figure 5.6 and 5.7 to flow from zinc to copper in the external circuit. This means that we are predicting the following redox reaction:

| | | |
|---|---|---|
| oxidation | $Zn(s) \rightarrow Zn^{2+}(aq) + 2e^-$ | $-E^\circ = +0.76$ V |
| reduction | $Cu^{2+}(aq) + 2e^- \rightarrow Cu(s)$ | $E^\circ = +0.34$ V |
| redox | $Cu^{2+}(aq) + Zn(s) \rightarrow Zn^{2+}(aq) + Cu(s)$ | $E = +1.10$ V |

Because $E$ is positive, the equation is written in the correct direction at standard conditions, although it does also allow us to speculate that it will go in this direction even if the conditions are not standard.

**Example 1**    Is potassium manganate(VII) strong enough as an oxidizing agent to oxidize a chloride to chlorine?

From the table of standard electrode reduction potentials:

① $\qquad 2Cl^-(aq) \rightarrow Cl_2(g) + 2e^- \qquad\qquad -E^\circ = -1.36$ V

② $MnO_4^-(aq) + 8H^+(aq) + 5e^- \rightarrow Mn^{2+}(aq) + 4H_2O(l) \qquad E^\circ = +1.50$ V

To produce the overall redox equation, we need to multiply ① by 5, and ② by 2 and add the equations together.

| | | |
|---|---|---|
| oxidation | $10Cl^-(aq) \rightarrow 5Cl_2(g) + 10e^-$ | $-E° = -1.36$ V |
| reduction | $2MnO_4^-(aq) + 16H^+(aq) + 10e^- \rightarrow 2Mn^{2+}(aq) + 8H_2O(l)$ | $E° = +1.50$ V |
| redox | $2MnO_4^-(aq) + 16H^+(aq) + 10Cl^-(aq) \rightarrow 5Cl_2(g) + 2Mn^{2+}(aq) + 8H_2O(l)$ | $E = +0.14$ V |

Chlorine is prepared in a fume cupboard by dropping concentrated hydrochloric acid onto solid manganate(VII) at room temperature. The redox equation as written does not predict the success of this preparation, but simply indicates the possibility of its success at standard conditions. Chlorine may also be prepared by warming a mixture of manganese dioxide and concentrated hydrochloric acid in spite of the fact that the redox equation under standard conditions yields a negative value for $E$.

**Example 2**    If sulphur dioxide is ̀ ᵻbled through a solution of potassium dichromate(VI), will it reduce the dichromate(VI) ion to the green chromium(III) ion?

From the table of standard electrode reduction potentials:

| | | |
|---|---|---|
| ① | $SO_3^{2-}(aq) + H_2O(l) \rightarrow SO_4^{2-}(aq) + 2H^+(aq) + 2e^-$ | $-E° = -0.20$ V |
| ② | $Cr_2O_7^{2-}(aq) + 14H^+(aq) + 6e^- \rightarrow 2Cr^{3+}(aq) + 7H_2O(l)$ | $E° = +1.33$ V |

Multiply ① by 3 and add the equations:

| | | |
|---|---|---|
| oxidation | $3SO_3^{2-}(aq) + 3H_2O(l) \rightarrow 3SO_4^{2-}(aq) + 6H^+(aq) + 6e^-$ | $-E° = -0.20$ V |
| reduction | $Cr_2O_7^{2-}(aq) + 14H^+(aq) + 6e^- \rightarrow 2Cr^{3+}(aq) + 7H_2O(l)$ | $E° = +1.33$ V |
| redox | $3SO_3^{2-}(aq) + Cr_2O_7^{2-}(aq) + 8H^+(aq) \rightarrow 3SO_4^{2-}(aq) + 2Cr^{3+}(aq) + 4H_2O(l)$ | $E = +1.13$ V |

We can say that the reaction will go under standard conditions and we may predict that it will go under the conditions of the experiment, but we cannot tell for sure. From experience we know that this reaction does in fact take place.

## 5.7 Electrolysis

When electricity is passed through a melt or an aqueous solution of a compound and decomposition of the compound occurs, the process is called **electrolysis**. We can use electrolysis to separate ionic compounds, but we must first consider the factors which affect the discharge of ions in these compounds.

**Position in the electrochemical series**

Figure 5.8

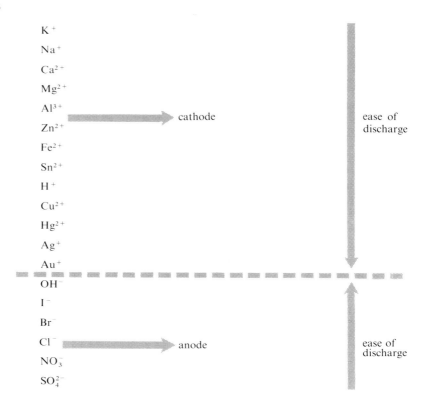

The ions discharge in reverse order of the electrochemical series. As you can see the hydroxide ion will discharge in preference to the chloride ion. The copper(II) ion will discharge in preference to the magnesium ion. This is known as **preferential discharge**.

**Concentration**

Let us consider the electrolysis of a sodium chloride solution.

$Na^+$ and $Cl^-$ from sodium chloride
$H^+$ and $OH^-$ from water

From the information given in Figure 5.8, we would expect the hydroxide ions to be discharged in preference to the chloride ions. However, the chloride ions are far more numerous than the hydroxide ions and they are discharged. This is called the **concentration effect**. In extremely dilute solutions, the hydroxide ions are discharged to a reasonable extent and a mixture of oxygen and chlorine is produced at the cathode.

**Type of electrode**

The choice of electrodes can control the discharge of ions. Let us consider again the electrolysis of sodium chloride. The ions present are $Na^+$, $Cl^-$, $H^+$, and $OH^-$. The alternatives are shown below.

*At platinum cathode*
$Na^+$ and $H^+$
$H^+$ will discharge in preference to $Na^+$.
$$2H^+(aq) + 2e^- \rightarrow H_2(g)$$

*At mercury cathode*
$Na^+$ and $H^+$
The $H^+$ should discharge in preference to $Na^+$, but the $Na^+$ could discharge in concentrated solution.
$$Na^+(aq) + 1e^- \rightarrow Na(s)$$
The sodium metal would then form an amalgam with the mercury.

When considering the discharge of ions from melts or aqueous solutions these three factors must be considered. Let us consider some examples of electrolysis.

**Electrolysis of dilute $H_2SO_4$ (pH = 0)**

**Figure 5.9** A Hofman voltameter is used for this experiment

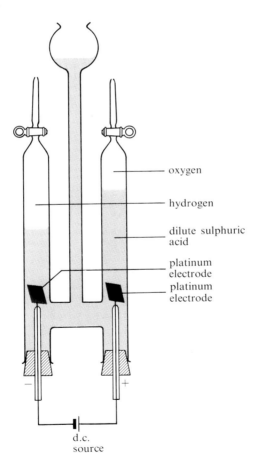

— oxygen

— hydrogen

— dilute sulphuric acid

— platinum electrode
— platinum electrode

d.c. source

*At cathode*                                              *At anode*
$H^+$

The hydrogen ions will accept electrons and hydrogen gas will be discharged

$$2H^+(aq) + 2e^- \rightarrow H_2(g)$$
$$4H^+(aq) + 4e^- \rightarrow 2H_2(g)$$                  $$2H_2O \rightarrow O_2(g) + 4H^+(aq) + 4e^-$$

At the anode oxygen gas is given off. The volume of oxygen is equal to
exactly half the volume of hydrogen. Since the solution of sulphuric acid
contains $OH^-$ ions to the extent of about $10^{-14}$ mol $l^{-1}$, it seems hardly
likely that the discharge of $OH^-$ ions could take place in sufficient quantity
to account for the oxygen gas evolved. We have to look for another
mechanism. If we consider the ions in solution and remember that they
carry an 'atmosphere' of water molecules with them, it seems plausible that
the water molecules will come in contact with the electrode first.

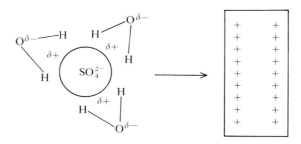

If the voltage being used is in excess of that suggested by $E^\circ$ values, then it
is the O—H bonds that are being broken and effectively the $O^{2-}$ ions
being discharged. In this type of electrolysis reaction, the half-equations in
Table D (page 189) provide us with possible mechanisms for electrode
reactions, but the $E^\circ$ values have little or no significance, since the voltages
being used are usually greatly in excess of those theoretically required to
discharge the ions involved.

**Electrolysis of dilute NaOH (pH ≈ 14)**

The apparatus used is that shown in Figure 5.9.

*At cathode*                                              *At anode*
                                                          $OH^-$

$$2H_2O(l) + 2e^- \rightarrow H_2(g) + 2OH^-(aq)$$     The $OH^-$ will discharge.
$$4H_2O(l) + 4e^- \rightarrow 2H_2(g) + 4OH^-(aq)$$    $$4OH^-(aq) \rightarrow O_2(g) + 2H_2O(l) + 4e^-$$

The volume of hydrogen liberated at the cathode is twice the volume of
oxygen liberated at the anode.

   Since the $H^+(aq)$ ion is present only to the extent of about $10^{-14}$ mol $l^{-1}$,
it seems as if it is the water molecules associated with the sodium ions
which are discharged. The $E^\circ$ values associated with this cathode reaction
apply at pH = 7 (which in this case it is not), but the equation does
provide a reasonable mechanism for the liberation of hydrogen.

**Electrolysis of NaCl(aq), (pH = 7)**

We will consider the electrolysis of solutions of different concentrations.

**1.** Sea water (very dilute sodium chloride)

*At cathode*
Hydrogen will be liberated in preference to sodium.

$$2H_2O(l) + 2e^- \rightarrow H_2(g) + 2OH^-(aq)$$

*At anode*
$Cl^-(aq)$ will be preferentially discharged, but there is also the possibility of $H_2O$ discharge.

$$2Cl^-(aq) \rightarrow Cl_2(g) + 2e^-$$
and
$$2H_2O(l) \rightarrow O_2(g) + 4H^+(aq) + 4e^-$$

The volumes of gases in this case have no simple relationship since the chlorine gas dissolves to a large extent in water forming hypochlorous and hydrochloric acids.

**2.** 1M sodium chloride

*At cathode*

$$2H_2O(l) + 2e^- \rightarrow H_2(g) + 2OH^-(aq)$$

*At anode*
The high concentration of $Cl^-(aq)$ ensures its preferential discharge.
$$2Cl^-(aq) \rightarrow Cl_2(g) + 2e^-$$

Equal volumes of hydrogen and chlorine are not obtained until the electrolysis has been running long enough for the solution to become saturated with chlorine.

**Electrolysis of CuSO₄ (pH = 3)**

**Figure 5.10** Apparatus for the electrolysis of $CuSO_4$

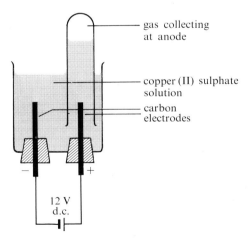

gas collecting at anode

copper (II) sulphate solution

carbon electrodes

12 V d.c.

*At cathode*

$$Cu^{2+}(aq) + 2e^- \rightarrow Cu(s)$$
$$2Cu^{2+}(aq) + 4e^- \rightarrow 2Cu(s)$$

*At anode*
$SO_4^{2-}(aq)$ is difficult to discharge and water is discharged in preference.

$$2H_2O(l) \rightarrow O_2(g) + 4H^+(aq) + 4e^-$$

Two moles of copper will be deposited at the cathode for every mole of oxygen liberated at the anode.

### 5.8 Extraction of metals

Certain metals can not be obtained from their oxides by chemical reduction. We can use the technique of electrolysis to extract metals from the ores.

**Electrolysis of molten NaCl**

The ions present are $Na^+$ and $Cl^-$.

*At cathode*
$Na^+$
The sodium ions accept electrons and discharge.
$$Na^+(l) + 1e^- \rightarrow Na(s)$$
$$2Na^+(l) + 2e^- \rightarrow 2Na(s)$$

*At anode*
$Cl^-$
The chloride ions give up electrons and discharge.

$$2Cl^-(l) \rightarrow Cl_2(g) + 2e^-$$

The more reactive metals are all obtained from their salts in this way.

**Aluminium**

Aluminium is extensively used today, and yet there was a time when it was more expensive than gold. This was because aluminium ores are unreactive. It was not until 1886 that a process was invented which enabled aluminium metal to be produced easily and cheaply provided that there was an inexpensive supply of electricity. The process is based on the most common ore of aluminium, bauxite, which is an impure form of aluminium oxide. The bauxite is treated chemically to produce pure aluminium oxide (alumina), which is then dissolved in molten cryolite $Na_3AlF_6$, another aluminium ore, and electrolysed as shown in Figure 5.11. The molten aluminium is tapped off and cast into ingots.

**Figure 5.11** Industrial manufacture of aluminium

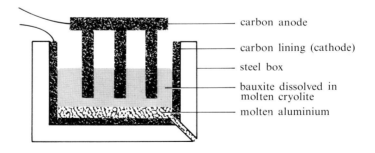

- carbon anode
- carbon lining (cathode)
- steel box
- bauxite dissolved in molten cryolite
- molten aluminium

The ions present are $Al^{3+}$, $Na^+$, $O^{2-}$, and $F^-$.

*At cathode*
$Al^{3+}$ and $Na^+$
$$Al^{3+}(l) + 3e^- \rightarrow Al(l)$$
$$4Al^{3+}(l) + 12e^- \rightarrow 4Al(l)$$

*At anode*
$O^{2-}$ and $F^-$
$$2O^{2-}(l) \rightarrow O_2(g) + 4e^-$$
$$6O^{2-}(l) \rightarrow 3O_2(g) + 12e^-$$

**Copper**    Impure copper can be refined using the apparatus shown in Figure 5.12.
The plate of pure copper is made at the cathode.

**Figure 5.12**

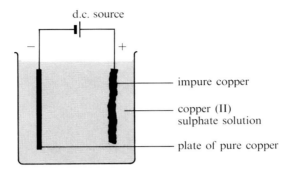

d.c. source

impure copper

copper (II)
sulphate solution

plate of pure copper

The ions present are $Cu^{2+}$, $SO_4^{2-}$, $H^+$, and $OH^-$.

*At cathode*
$Cu^{2+}(aq) + 2e^- \rightarrow Cu(s)$

*At anode*
The anode is positively charged and
therefore electron seeking. There are
three possible ways for the anode to
obtain electrons.

1    Remove electrons from $H_2O(l)$.
2    Remove electrons from $SO_4^{2-}(aq)$
ions.
3    Remove electrons from a copper
atom and release the resulting cop-
per(II) ion into the solution.

The reaction which requires the least
energy will be the one preferred, and
in this case it is the third possibility.
$Cu(s) \rightarrow Cu^{2+}(aq) + 2e^-$

The copper in the impure copper is losing electrons and forming $Cu^{2+}(aq)$
ions, which are attracted to the cathode where they accept two electrons to
form Cu(s). This electrolysis will continue until all the copper has been
removed from the impure metal. It is a well-known way of purifying a
metal. The pure metal is always made the cathode. In the case of copper,
the impurities form a sludge at the bottom of the reaction vessel. This
sludge contains gold and silver which, when extracted, go a considerable
way to paying for the purification process.

**Summary**

From this chapter you should know:

1   That oxidation is a loss of electrons.

2   That reduction is a gain of electrons.

3   How to construct a redox equation.

4   How to show that redox has occurred.

5   The meaning of the electrode potential.

6   That the hydrogen electrode is used to determine $E°$ values.

7   How to calculate the e.m.f. of a cell.

8   That redox can be used to predict the possibility of reaction occurring.

9   Electrolysis and preferential discharge.

10   Extraction of metals.

**Questions**

1   Write ion-electron equations, and then a balanced equation for the over-all reaction, for the oxidation and reduction processes which occur when copper reacts as follows:
1   Copper metal is added to dilute nitric acid; a blue solution is formed and nitric oxide is evolved.
2   Copper metal is added to silver nitrate solution. *SCEEB*

2   1   A sample of calcium on prolonged exposure to the air was found to have changed to a white powder.
1.1   What is this powder most likely to be? Justify your answer.
1.2   Outline a method by which it would be possible to reconvert the white powder to calcium.

2   Use the table of Standard Reduction Electrode Potentials (table D on page 189) to answer the following questions:
2.1   What would be the e.m.f. of a zinc-silver cell under standard conditions?
2.2   Name a reagent which you would expect to be effective in converting iodide ions in aqueous solution to iodine, but not bromide ions to bromine. How would you detect that iodine had been formed?
2.3   What happens to a solution of sulphur dioxide when it is left exposed to the air? What chemical test would you carry out to show that this had happened?
2.4   What do you predict would happen if bromine were added to a solution of $Hg^{2+}$ (aq) ions?
Give a reason for your answer.
2.5   Why can an iron(II) compound be classed as both an oxidizing and a reducing agent? *SCEEB*

3    (You may find the data in Data table D on page 189 useful in answering this question.)

The purple permanganate ion, $MnO_4^-(aq)$, reacts with the almost colourless manganese(II) ion, $Mn^{2+}(aq)$, with the production of the brown solid, manganese(IV) oxide, $MnO_2$.

The half-reactions and the corresponding $E°$ values are:

$$MnO_2(s) + 4H^+(aq) + 2e^- \rightarrow Mn^{2+}(aq) + 2H_2O \qquad E° = +1.23\ V$$

$$MnO_4^-(aq) + 4H^+(aq) + 3e^- \rightarrow MnO_2(s) + 2H_2O \qquad E° = +1.67\ V$$

1    A pupil uses the apparatus shown below to couple these reactions into a cell.

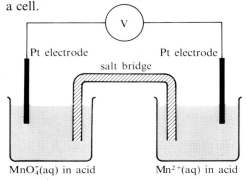

1.1    In which direction will electrons flow through the meter?

1.2    Which solution will act as oxidizing agent?

1.3    What *two* properties would a substance require to make it a suitable 'bridge solution'?

1.4    What e.m.f. would the pupil calculate for the cell from the equations?

1.5    Suggest a reason why he would not obtain this value on the voltmeter V.

2    When a solution of manganese(II) sulphate is electrolysed between platinum electrodes, a purple colour appears at the anode.

2.1    What species causes the purple colour? Give an ion-electron equation for its production from the $Mn^{2+}(aq)$ ion.

2.2    Why does the purple colour appear at the anode and not at the cathode?

2.3    What ion might be discharged at the cathode? Give an ion-electron equation for the process.

3    You are given four wires: magnesium, silver, tin and zinc. They are similar in appearance, and you have to find out which is which. How would you try to do this if you had available in addition to the wires only a centre-zero galvanometer, and a beaker of dilute potassium nitrate solution? *SCEEB*

4    The half-reaction $O_2(g) + 2H^+(aq) + 2e^- \rightarrow H_2O_2(l)$ has a Standard Reduction Electrode Potential of $+0.68\ V$.

Which *one* of the following reagents should be able to convert hydrogen peroxide ($H_2O_2$) into oxygen gas? (Use page 189 of the Data tables.)

$Fe^{3+}(aq);\ Fe^{2+}(aq);\ Sn^{4+}(aq);\ Sn^{2+}(aq).$

For the reagent you choose, write a half-reaction equation showing its reaction. *SCEEB*

5   Use the information in the Data tables (page 189) to answer this question. The half-reaction equation for the reduction of the titanium(III) ion to titanium(II) ion is

$$Ti^{3+}(aq) + e^- \rightarrow Ti^{2+}(aq) \qquad E° = -0.37 \text{ V}$$

Which one of the following could be used as a reducing agent in this case?

(a) $Fe^{2+}(aq)$     (b) $Zn(s)$     (c) $MnO_4^-(aq)$.

Write a half-reaction equation for the oxidation of the reagent you choose.
*SCEEB*

6   Which pairs of the following metals could be used to give a cell whose voltage under standard conditions is between 0.4 and 0.5 volts? Copper, silver, tin and zinc. *P & W*

7   1   Construct an ion electron half equation for the change $XeO_3 \rightarrow Xe$.
    2   Is the change $CO_2 \rightarrow CO_3^{2-}$ oxidation, reduction or neither?
    3   Give an example of a reaction where hydrogen is reduced. *P & W*

8                       $Fe^{3+}(aq) + e^- \rightarrow Fe^{2+}(aq)$                    0.77 V

$$MnO_4^-(aq) + 8H^+(aq) + 5e^- \rightarrow Mn^{2+}(aq) + 4H_2O \qquad 1.51 \text{ V}$$

Write a balanced equation to represent the reaction of the iron(II) ion with acidified permanganate solution and calculate the voltage which can be obtained if the reaction is used under standard conditions as the basis of a cell. *P & W*

# 6 The Periodic Table

## 6.1 Arrangement of the elements

Up to the year 1800 only thirty-four elements were known. By 1870 this number had almost doubled, and by 1974 the figure was 105. The belief that all systems had a certain degree of order led to the idea that these elements could be arranged in a definite way.

In 1817, J. W. Döbereiner (1780–1849) observed that certain elements had similar chemical properties and he found that he could group them in threes:

| Lithium | Calcium | Chlorine |
| Sodium | Strontium | Bromine |
| Potassium | Barium | Iodine |

He called these groups 'triads', and this was the first attempt to arrange the elements in some kind of order.

By 1863 many more elements had been discovered. J. Newlands arranged the elements in order of their relative atomic masses. He divided the elements into groups of seven, as he found that every eighth element had properties similar to the first element of the preceding series.

| Li | Be | B | C | N | O | F |
| Na | Mg | Al | Si | P | S | Cl |
| K | Ca | Cr | Ti | Mn | Fe | |

Newlands called these groups 'octaves'. This method did produce a degree of regularity, but the great disadvantage of this system was that, as new elements were discovered, they could not be fitted into the octave structure.

In 1864 Lothar Meyer (1830–95) plotted a graph of atomic volume against relative atomic mass (Figure 6.1). The atomic volume of an element is the relative atomic mass divided by the density of the element.

You can see from the graph that the elements with similar properties recur at approximately the same point in each part of the graph. The noble gases neon, argon, and krypton are all at similar positions on the graph, which would indicate that there is a relation between the properties of the elements and their relative atomic mass.

Dimitri Mendeleev (1839–1907) used increasing relative atomic mass, in conjunction with similar chemical properties, as the basis for arranging the elements. His table was constructed in such a way that gaps were left where the pattern would otherwise be destroyed. He predicted the properties of these elements, as then undiscovered, quite accurately.

Mendeleev's table is similar to the one in use today, but it was H. Moseley who put the table into the present form. Moseley worked with X-rays and found that the energy of the X-rays produced by an element increased as the relative atomic mass increased. He could not, however, obtain an exact relation between the relative atomic mass and the energy of the X-rays, so he assigned a number to each element according to its position in the Periodic Table. This number, which he called the **atomic**

**Figure 6.1** Graph of atomic volume against relative atomic mass

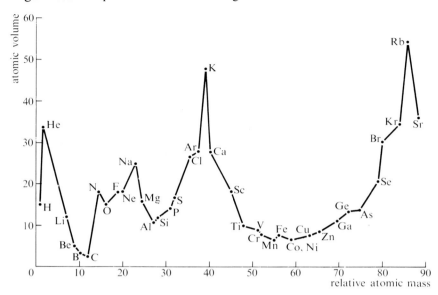

**number**, is the number of protons (or the number of electrons) in a neutral atom. Using the atomic number, Moseley was able to obtain an exact relation with the energy of the X-rays produced.

**Figure 6.2** The modern form of the Periodic Table

| | group 1 | group 2 | | | | | | transition series | | | | | group 3 | group 4 | group 5 | group 6 | group 7 | group 8 |
|---|---|---|---|---|---|---|---|---|---|---|---|---|---|---|---|---|---|---|---|
| | 1 | 2 | | | | | number of electrons in the highest energy level | | | | | | 3 | 4 | 5 | 6 | 7 | 8 |
| period 1 | 1 H | | | | | | | | | | | | | | | | | | 2 He |
| period 2 | 3 Li | 4 Be | | | | | | | | | | | 5 B | 6 C | 7 N | 8 O | 9 F | 10 Ne |
| period 3 | 11 Na | 12 Mg | | | | | | | | | | | 13 Al | 14 Si | 15 P | 16 S | 17 Cl | 18 Ar |
| period 4 | 19 K | 20 Ca | 21 Sc | 22 Ti | 23 V | 24 Cr | 25 Mn | 26 Fe | 27 Co | 28 Ni | 29 Cu | 30 Zn | 31 Ga | 32 Ge | 33 As | 34 Se | 35 Br | 36 Kr |

The Periodic Table as we know it today is shown in Figure 6.2. The **periods** run from left to right horizontally, and each element has an atomic number one unit greater than the preceding element. For example, Period 2 contains the following elements.

| | | | | | | | | |
|---|---|---|---|---|---|---|---|---|
| period 2 | 3 Li | 4 Be | | 5 B | 6 C | 7 N | 8 O | 9 F | 10 Ne |

The **groups** run from top to bottom and contain elements with the same number of electrons in their highest energy levels. Members of Group 1, Li, Na, and K have one electron in the highest energy level. Members of Group 2, Be, Mg, and Ca have two electrons in the highest energy level.

Group 1    Li (2.1)    Na (2.8.1)    K (2.8.8.1)
Group 2    Be (2.2)    Mg (2.8.2)    Ca (2.8.8.2)

It can be shown that elements in the same group have similar properties. For example, the elements in Group 1 are all reactive metals. The Group 8 elements all have eight electrons in the highest energy level, with the exception of helium, which has two. The Group 8 elements were called 'inert gases', meaning that they were completely unreactive. It has been discovered that they do react under certain special circumstances, and they are now called the **noble gases**. The lack of reactivity of these elements is normally attributed to the fact that there are eight electrons in the highest energy level. These eight electrons are often referred to as a **stable octet**. When other elements react, they usually do so in such a way as to obtain this stable octet. It is very important to remember this when we consider the bonding of elements.

The graph in Figure 6.3 shows the atomic number of elements plotted against the number of electrons in the highest energy level. You will see that all members of Group 8 are on the peaks of the graph, and that all the members of the other groups occur at exactly the same position on the graph. All elements with three electrons in the highest energy level belong to Group 3. By reading across the graph you can obtain the other groups in the Periodic Table, and by reading from the bottom to the top of each peak, you will obtain the periods in the Periodic Table.

**Figure 6.3** Graph of atomic number against number of electrons in highest energy level

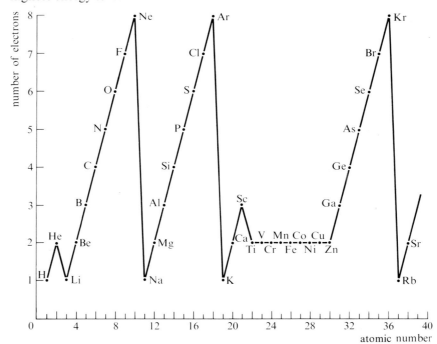

## 6.2 Trends in physical properties

Consideration of some of the physical properties of the first twenty elements of the Periodic Table helps to demonstrate the periodicity of the elements.

**Atomic size**
The **atomic volume** is defined as the volume occupied in the solid state by one mole of the element at its melting point. This measurement does not give a reliable prediction of the size of a single atom because elements tend to differ in the way their atoms are packed in a solid. A more reliable tool for the prediction of the size of a single atom is the covalent radius, deduced from the measurement of inter-atomic spacings by means of X-rays. The covalent radius is half the distance between the centres of adjacent bonded atoms.

**Figure 6.4** Covalent radius measured in nanometres $(m \times 10^{-9})$

| H 0.037 | | | | | | | He — |
|---|---|---|---|---|---|---|---|
| Li 0.123 | Be 0.089 | B 0.08 | C 0.077 | N 0.074 | O 0.074 | F 0.072 | Ne — |
| Na 0.157 | Mg 0.136 | Al 0.125 | Si 0.117 | P 0.110 | S 0.104 | Cl 0.099 | Ar — |
| K 0.203 | Ca 0.174 | | | | | | |

Figure 6.4 shows that:

1 In any period the atomic size decreases from left to right.
2 In any group the atomic size increases from top to bottom.
3 There is no covalent radius for the noble gases.

From this we can deduce that:

1 In any period the increase in the nuclear charge of successive elements causes a marked increase in the element's attraction for electrons.
2 In any group the atoms increase in size as another level of electrons shields the outer electrons from the nucleus.

**Melting point and boiling point**
**Figure 6.5** Melting points and boiling points measured in kelvin (K)

| m.p. | 14 | | | | | | | 1 |
|---|---|---|---|---|---|---|---|---|
| symbol | H | | | | | | | He |
| b.p. | 21 | | | | | | | 4 |
| | 453 | 1551 | 2573 | 3823 | 63 | 55 | 53 | 24 |
| | Li | Be | B | C | N | O | F | Ne |
| | 1590 | 3243 | 2823 | 5100 | 77 | 90 | 85 | 27 |
| | 371 | 922 | 933 | 1683 | 317 | 386 | 172 | 84 |
| | Na | Mg | Al | Si | P | S | Cl | Ar |
| | 1156 | 1363 | 2740 | 2628 | 553 | 718 | 238 | 87 |
| | 337 | 1113 | | | | | | |
| | K | Ca | | | | | | |
| | 1047 | 1757 | | | | | | |

Figure 6.5 shows that:

1 There is a tendency for melting points and boiling points of solid elements to increase towards the right, and for the melting points and boiling points of gaseous elements to decrease towards the right.
2 Melting points and boiling points decrease in a group from top to bottom for solids, and increase from top to bottom for gases. The alkali metals (Li, Na, and K) show this for solids, and the noble gases show this for gases.

From left to right, the inter-atomic bonds must be increasing in strength for the solids, and the inter-molecular bonds must be decreasing for the gases. In a group the inter-atomic bonds must be decreasing in strength for solids and the inter-molecular bonds must be increasing in strength for gases.

**Ionization energies**    The energy required to remove a mole of electrons from a mole of neutral, isolated gaseous atoms is called the **first ionization energy**.

$$Mg(g) \rightarrow Mg^+(g) + e^- \qquad \Delta H_1 = +738 \text{ kJ mol}^{-1}$$

The energy required to remove another mole of electrons from the new ions is called the **second ionization energy**.

$$Mg^+(g) \rightarrow Mg^{2+}(g) + e^- \qquad \Delta H_2 = +1450 \text{ kJ mol}^{-1}$$

**Figure 6.6** Ionization energies measured in kJ mol$^{-1}$

| symbol | H | | | | | | | He |
|---|---|---|---|---|---|---|---|---|
| 1st ionization energy | 1312 | | | | | | | 2362 |
| 2nd ionization energy | — | | | | | | | 5250 |
| 3rd ionization energy | — | | | | | | | — |
| 4th ionization energy | — | | | | | | | — |
| | Li | Be | B | C | N | O | F | Ne |
| | 520 | 899 | 801 | 1086 | 1402 | 1314 | 1681 | 2080 |
| | 7297 | 1757 | 2427 | 2352 | 2856 | 3388 | 3376 | 3717 |
| | 11787 | 14845 | 3659 | 4620 | 4577 | 5296 | 6045 | 6128 |
| | — | 21003 | 25022 | 6222 | 7474 | 7468 | 8409 | 9362 |
| | Na | Mg | Al | Si | P | S | Cl | Ar |
| | 496 | 738 | 577 | 786 | 1012 | 999 | 1255 | 1520 |
| | 4563 | 1450 | 1816 | 1577 | 1903 | 2258 | 2297 | 2665 |
| | 6920 | 7733 | 2744 | 3232 | 2910 | 3378 | 3850 | 3647 |
| | 9542 | 10546 | 11576 | 4353 | 4956 | 4563 | 5163 | 5770 |
| | K | Ca | | | | | | |
| | 419 | 590 | | | | | | |
| | 3070 | 1145 | | | | | | |
| | 4439 | 4942 | | | | | | |
| | 5877 | 6466 | | | | | | |

Data table B in this book gives values for most elements in the Periodic Table.

Figure 6.6 shows that:

1 In any period the first ionization energy increases from left to right.

2    In any group the first ionization energy decreases from top to bottom.
3    The first ionization energy is large for the noble gases.
4    There is a large increase in the next ionization energy after the ion has reached the configuration of a noble gas, e.g. in the 2nd ionization energy for sodium and in the 3rd ionization energy for magnesium.

From this we can deduce that:

1    In any period the increase in nuclear charge makes the electron more difficult to remove.
2    In any group the addition of another level of electrons shields the outer electrons from the nucleus.
3    The noble gases have a stable electron arrangement.
4    The shielding effect is no longer present when the ion has reached the stable configuration of a noble gas.

**Electron affinity**    The energy released when a neutral gaseous atom attracts and combines with an additional electron to form a negative ion is called the **electron affinity**.

$$Cl(g) + e^- \rightarrow Cl^-(g) \qquad \Delta H = -362 \text{ kJ mol}^{-1}$$

Values for electron affinities are difficult to obtain and indeed they apply only to atoms which require to accept electrons to obtain the structure of a noble gas.

Table 6.1 shows electron affinity values for the halogens measured in kJ mol$^{-1}$.

**Table 6.1**

| Halogen | Electron affinity (kJ mol$^{-1}$) | Covalent radius (nm) | Ionic radius (nm) |
|---------|-----------|----------|-------|
| F  | −347 | 0.072 | 0.133 |
| Cl | −362 | 0.099 | 0.181 |
| Br | −341 | 0.114 | 0.196 |
| I  | −309 | 0.133 | 0.220 |

Table 6.1 shows that:

1    The electron affinity decreases from chlorine to bromine to iodine.
2    The electron affinity of fluorine is unexpectedly small.

From this we can deduce that:

1    As the atom size increases, the shielding effect becomes greater and the distance of the attracted electron from the nucleus increases.
2    The fluorine atom is very small and the nuclear charge is also small, so that the attracted electron causes a large increase in the size of the ion. This is difficult to understand unless you are familiar with the inverse square law, which states that the force of attraction is proportional to the product of the charge values and inversely proportional to the square of the distance between them.

$$\text{Force of attraction} = \frac{\text{nuclear charge} \times \text{electron charge}}{(\text{ionic radius})^2}$$

Electron affinity values considered with ionization energy values can help to predict which atoms may remove electrons from others. We shall deal with the displacement of the halogens later in the chapter.

**Attraction of nucleus for electrons** The electronegativity of an element is a measure of the attraction that an atom of the element has for the shared electrons when the element is in a combined state.

**Figure 6.7** Electronegativity measured on the Pauling scale

| H 2.1 | | | | | | | He — |
|---|---|---|---|---|---|---|---|
| Li 1.0 | Be 1.5 | B 2.0 | C 2.5 | N 3.0 | O 3.5 | F 4.0 | Ne — |
| Na 0.9 | Mg 1.2 | Al 1.5 | Si 1.8 | P 2.1 | S 2.5 | Cl 3.0 | Ar — |
| K 0.8 | Ca 1.0 | | | | | | |

Figure 6.7 shows that:

1 In any period the electronegativities increase from left to right.
2 In any group the electronegativities decrease from top to bottom.
3 There is no value for the electronegativity of noble gases.

From this we can deduce that:

1 In any period, increase in nuclear charge makes that nucleus more electron attracting.
2 In any group the addition of another level of electrons shields the outer electrons from the nucleus, and so they are not attracted as strongly.
3 The noble gases are electrically stable.

The trends and deductions drawn from Figure 6.6 ionization energies and Figure 6.7 electronegativities are virtually the same, but the real significance of the electronegativities lies in their use to predict the nature of a bond by considering the electronegativity values for the elements concerned. Large differences indicate ionic bonding and the smaller the value the nearer the bond is to being pure covalent as in the case of the chlorine molecule.

100% ionic $Li^+Cl^-$ ⟸ ⟹ 100% convalent $Cl_2$

**Example** Compare the bonds in the following substances:

|  | NaCl | HCl | $Cl_2$ |
|---|---|---|---|
| $\Delta E.N.$ | 2.1 ionic | 0.9 polar | 0 covalent |
|  | CaO | $H_2O$ | $O_2$ |
| $\Delta E.N.$ | 2.5 ionic | 1.4 polar | 0 covalent |

$\Delta E.N.$ is the difference in the electronegativities of the elements in the compounds.

It is important to remember that electronegativity differences help to predict the nature of a bond, and that it is necessary to look at all the bonds and the distribution of charge before predicting whether the molecule is polar or not. Tetrachloromethane, $CCl_4$, has four polar bonds, but the distribution in space renders the molecule non-polar.

### 6.3 Trends in bonding in elements

The elements on the left-hand side of the Periodic Table are typically **metallic** in character. Their structure is that of closely packed atoms with free outer electrons. This accounts for their typical metallic properties—high boiling point, good thermal and electrical conductivity, metallic lustre, malleability and ductility.

The elements on the right-hand side of the Periodic Table are typically **non-metallic** in character. Their structure is that of discrete covalent molecules with weak Van der Waals' forces between them. This accounts for their typical non-metallic properties—low melting and boiling points, poor thermal and electrical conductivity.

The elements in the middle are the 'in-betweens'. Their structure is that of clusters of covalently bonded atoms, which accounts for their high melting points and boiling points. Carbon displays different structures in its two polymorphs—graphite which conducts like a metal and diamond which behaves like a typical non-metal.

### 6.4 Hydrogen bonding

Water has the formula $H_2O$. Electronegativity values indicate that the O—H bond is polar. The molecule has an asymmetric distribution of charge, causing a resultant dipole.

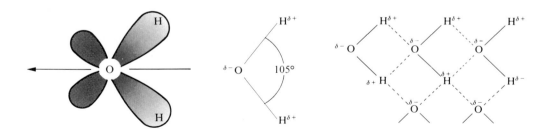

In liquid water the molecules attract each other and these forces of attraction are called **hydrogen bonds**. From a molecular weight of 18, we might have expected water to be a gas like hydrogen sulphide, $H_2S$, but the existence of hydrogen bonds between the molecules means that the inter-molecular forces are considerably greater than Van der Waals' forces. This explains why the boiling point of water is higher than we might have expected.

In the solid phase, the hydrogen bonding is responsible for the highly symmetrical shapes seen in snow flakes, Figure 6.8, and it causes ice to have a very open structure, which makes it less dense than water.

**Figure 6.8**

Many compounds with hydroxyl groups in them have properties consistent with hydrogen bonding.

**Example 1**    Sulphuric acid is viscous and has a high boiling point, 270 °C.

$$\cdots\overset{\delta-}{O}\diagdown \overset{\delta-}{O}\!\!-\!\!\overset{\delta+}{H}\cdots\cdots\overset{\delta-}{O}\diagdown \overset{\delta-}{O}\!\!-\!\!\overset{\delta+}{H}\cdots\cdots\overset{\delta-}{O}$$

This diagram shows how two molecules of sulphuric acid could attract each other, but it is an oversimplification of a three-dimensional system.

**Example 2**    Propane-1,2,3-triol (glycerol) is viscous and has a high boiling point, 290 °C.

Again this diagram is an oversimplification of the attraction between oppositely charged parts of the three-dimensional molecule.

**Example 3**    Solubility of compounds in water.

Water is a rather remarkable compound in that it dissolves so many different substances. This can be attributed to the polar nature of the water molecule.

**The fountain experiment**    As soon as the first drop of water enters the flask, it dissolves enough hydrogen chloride to reduce the pressure in the flask. This causes the water to come in to the flask faster, dissolving more gas which, in turn, causes more water to come up to the flask. This gives the effect of a fountain.

**Figure 6.9**

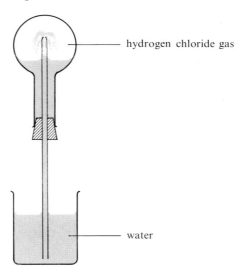

hydrogen chloride gas

water

Dry hydrogen chloride gas is extremely soluble in water, as this experiment shows. This can be explained quite readily when it is appreciated that both hydrogen chloride and water are polar molecules.

$$H^{\delta+}—Cl^{\delta-} \qquad \overset{H}{\underset{H}{\diagdown}}_{\delta+} O^{\delta-} \qquad H^{\delta+}—Cl^{\delta-} \qquad \overset{H}{\underset{H}{\diagdown}}_{\delta+} O^{\delta-}$$

The hydrogen chloride and water molecules line up so that there is an attraction between the molecules. The molecules flip into the correct orientations and attract each other strongly. The fountain experiment also works very well with ammonia gas because this compound is also polar and extremely soluble in water.

When an ionic compound is put into water, the extent to which it dissolves depends on:

1    The relative sizes of the forces holding the ions together in the crystal.
2    The forces of attraction of the water molecules on the ions.

Since sodium chloride dissolves easily in water (Figure 6.10) the forces of attraction between the ions are smaller than those of the water molecules on the ions.

As calcium carbonate is sparingly soluble in water, the forces between the ions in the crystal are greater than the forces pulling the ions into solution. However, some substances like sodium hydroxide dissolve in water with the evolution of heat, whereas others, like potassium nitrate take in heat as they dissolve. Pulling the ions out of the crystal lattice is an endothermic process and the solvation of the ion is an exothermic process. The heat of solution is the algebraic sum of these two quantities and can be either positive or negative.

**Figure 6.10** Solvation of ions

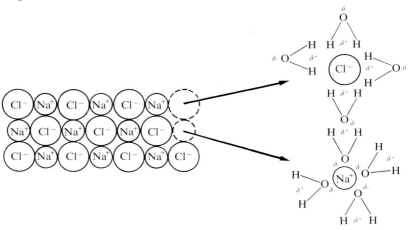

**Example 4**    Non-polar compounds, like tetrachloromethane do not dissolve in water, since there is no attraction between the molecules of the compound and the molecules of water.

**Figure 6.11**

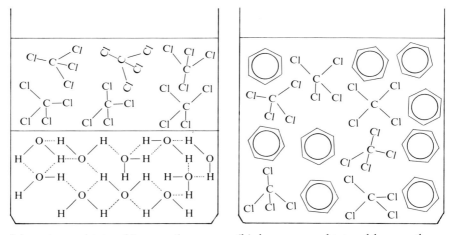

(a) water and tetrachloromethane    (b) benzene and tetrachloromethane

On the other hand non-polar compounds are miscible with each other simply because there are no attractions other than Van der Waals' forces between the molecules.

## 6.5 Chlorides

To show the periodic variation in the properties of compounds, we will first consider the compounds formed when chlorine reacts with elements in groups 1 to 7. Chlorine is one of the extremely reactive non-metals. It is found in group 7 of the Periodic Table, and so has seven electrons in its highest energy level.

Chlorine reacts violently with the group 1 metals to give highly stable, crystalline solids such as lithium, sodium, and potassium chlorides, LiCl, NaCl, and KCl respectively. These metal chlorides display the characteristic properties of ionic compounds. They have high boiling points, they dissolve in water, and they conduct electricity when molten or in aqueous solution. Their structure is that of a giant lattice of positive metal ions and negative non-metal ions, as illustrated in section 6.8. Chlorine reacts in a similar fashion with the group 2 metals to form beryllium, magnesium, and calcium chloride, $BeCl_2$, $MgCl_2$, and $CaCl_2$ respectively.

The group 3 chlorides are more covalent in nature, the first one in the series, boron trichloride $BCl_3$, being completely covalent. Boron trichloride and aluminium chloride $Al_2Cl_6$ are both volatile, suggesting that they consist of discrete covalent molecules. The group 4 chlorides, tetrachloromethane $CCl_4$ and silicon tetrachloride $SiCl_4$ are also covalent. They are liquids with characteristic low boiling points and do not conduct electricity. From earlier chapters we know that tetrachloromethane does not mix (it is **immiscible**) with water. Silicon tetrachloride, however, reacts with water. The explanation for this is that the silicon atom in $SiCl_4$ is very much larger than the carbon atom in $CCl_4$, so the chlorine atoms in the molecule are spaced further apart.

The group 5 chlorides, nitrogen trichloride $NCl_3$ and phosphorus trichloride $PCl_3$, are also covalent liquids which hydrolyse. The elements in group 6 and group 7 form covalent chlorides which are very unstable.

The trends in the chlorides of the first twenty elements are clear. Those on the left-hand side of the Periodic Table are stable and ionic, those on the right-hand side are unstable and covalent, and those in between are intermediate in character.

## 6.6  Oxides

The reactions of oxygen with the elements in groups 1 to 7 should also show periodic variations.

Basic oxides    Metal oxides, which react with acids to form salts and water only, are called basic oxides. They are ionic solids with high melting points and boiling points. The basic oxides of metals at the upper end of the reactivity series are soluble in water producing alkaline solutions, while the others are insoluble.

$$Na_2O(s) + H_2O(l) \rightarrow 2NaOH(aq)$$
$$\text{sodium hydroxide}$$

Acidic oxides    Non-metals burn in oxygen to form covalent compounds, usually gases ($CO_2$, $SO_2$, $NO_2$) or solids of low melting point ($SO_3$, $P_2O_5$), which dissolve in water to form acids. $SiO_2$ forms a giant network and is an exception.

$$CO_2(g) + H_2O(l) \rightarrow H_2CO_3(aq)$$
$$\text{carbonic acid}$$

$$P_2O_5(s) + 3H_2O(l) \rightarrow 2H_3PO_4(aq)$$
$$\text{phosphoric acid}$$

Neutral oxides    Some oxides show **neither** acidic **nor** basic properties. They are insoluble in water and have no corresponding salts. Examples include carbon monoxide, water, and dinitrogen oxide.

Amphoteric oxides    These are the oxides of metals, such as beryllium, aluminium, zinc, lead, and tin. They react **both** as acidic **and** basic oxides depending on the conditions.

Aluminium oxide reacts with hydrochloric acid to form a solution of aluminium chloride,

$$Al_2O_3(s) + 6HCl(aq) \rightarrow 2Al^{3+}(aq) + 6Cl^-(aq) + 3H_2O(l)$$

whereas it dissolves in sodium hydroxide solution to form a solution of sodium aluminate.

$$Al_2O_3(s) + 2NaOH(aq) \rightarrow 2Na^+(aq) + 2AlO_2^-(aq) + H_2O(l)$$

**Structure of $SiO_2$**    Carbon dioxide and silicon dioxide look as though they ought to have similar properties and indeed we shall see that chemically they do, but a look at the physical properties will show marked differences. Carbon dioxide if subjected to about 5 atm pressure, will condense and freeze at $-56\,°C$. Liquid carbon dioxide will boil at $-78\,°C$ if the pressure is released forming solid and gas simultaneously and we are left with a solid which sublimes at $-78\,°C$.

Silicon dioxide is a white crystalline solid and it is found as white sand, quartz and mica. When we consider the melting point $1610\,°C$ and the boiling point $2200\,°C$, we can see at once that we are not dealing with the breaking of Van der Waals' forces, but the breaking of covalent bonds themselves. Silicon dioxide forms a large network structure in the same way as diamond using the oxygen atoms of its neighbours to achieve it.

**Figure 6.12**

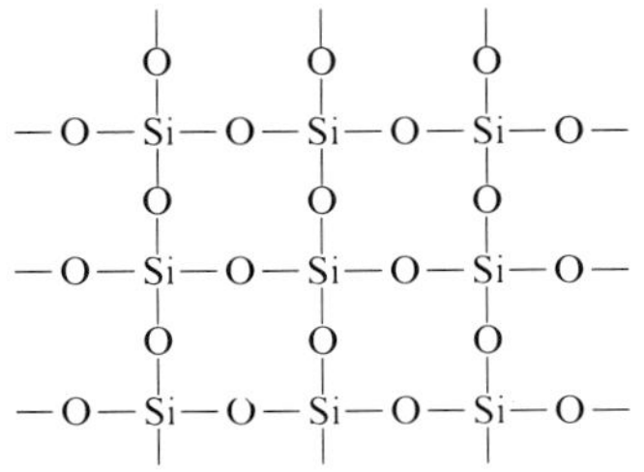

To envisage the structure of quartz we have to see this figure with the bonds tetrahedral, so that each of the eight-membered rings becomes non-planar.

Periodicity in
the oxides

**Figure 6.13**

| $Li_2O$ | BeO | $B_2O_3$ | $CO_2$ | $N_2O_5$ | $O_2$ | $F_2O_7$ |
|---|---|---|---|---|---|---|
| basic | amphoteric | weakly acidic | | acidic | | strongly acidic |
| ionic | | covalent | | | | |

| $Na_2O$ | MgO | $Al_2O_3$ | $SiO_2$ | $P_4O_{10}$ | $SO_2$ | $Cl_2O_7$ |
|---|---|---|---|---|---|---|
| strongly basic | basic | amphoteric | weakly acidic | | acidic | strongly acidic |
| ionic | | | covalent network | covalent | | |

As we move from left to right across the Periodic Table, there is a change from basic through amphoteric to acidic oxides, as shown in Figure 6.13. Note also that $Na_2O$ is more basic than $Li_2O$, MgO is more basic than BeO, $Al_2O_3$ is more basic than $B_2O_3$, and so on. In general, basic character is increasing as we move down the group.

### 6.7 Hydrides

In the course of our studies we have come across a number of compounds of hydrogen, which we have not really considered as hydrides. For example, $H_2O$, $H_2S$, HCl, HBr, HI, $CH_4$ are all hydrides of non-metals and we reconcile the bonding in these molecules by envisaging the overlapping of electron clouds to give hydrogen the electron arrangement of helium. Since we associate bonding with the structure of the noble gases, logic demands that the $H^-$ ion is a likely species. When an alkali metal is fused in the presence of hydrogen, the elements react to form a compound.

$$2Na(l) + H_2(g) \rightarrow 2NaH(s)$$

Sodium hydride conducts electricity when molten and liberates sodium at the cathode and hydrogen at the anode, justifying the prediction of the $H^-$ ion. This chemistry is general for group I and group II hydrides. Boron and aluminium form hydrides with empirical formulae $BH_3$ and $AlH_3$, but they are solids which would seem to suggest association of the molecules through hydrogen bonding.

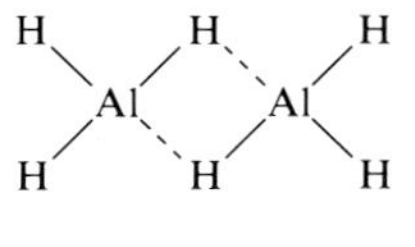

They burn spontaneously in air to form oxides and are hydrolysed slowly by water liberating hydrogen.

$$2Al_2H_6(s) + 6O_2(g) \rightarrow 2Al_2O_3(s) + 6H_2O(l)$$

$$Al_2H_6(s) + 6H_2O(l) \rightarrow 2Al(OH)_3 + 3H_2$$

The hydrides of carbon will be studied as hydrocarbons in chapter 8, but we must consider whether the chemistry of silicon is analogous to that of carbon. The silanes $Si_nH_{2n+2}$, exist for values of n up to 6, but they are unstable and ignite spontaneously in air

$$SiH_4(g) + 2O_2(g) \rightarrow SiO_2(s) + 2H_2O(g)$$

Ammonia is a hydride of nitrogen and it is a well known base. The chemistry of ammonia is usually explained in terms of the lone pair of electrons on the nitrogen. The analogous hydride of phosphorus, phosphine $PH_3$ also has a lone pair of electrons on the phosphorus atom and we might therefore expect the properties of phosphine to resemble those of ammonia. In the event however we find that phosphine is insoluble in water and does not form the $PH_4^+$ ion easily and that it burns spontaneously in air. We can explain this either by comparing the radii of nitrogen and phosphorus, or by comparing their electronegativities. The P—H bond appears to be weaker than the N—H bond.

Although water, oxygen hydride, is a neutral liquid, the analogous hydride of sulphur, hydrogen sulphide is an evil-smelling gas, which dissolves in water to form a weak acid.

$$H_2S(g) + H_2O(l) \rightleftharpoons H^+(aq) + HS^-(aq)$$

The lack of hydrogen bonding in hydrogen sulphide can be attributed to the fact that the sulphur atom is much bigger than the oxygen atom.

The chemistry of the halogen hydrides will be dealt with in detail later in this chapter.

**Periodicity in the hydrides**

**Figure 6.14**

| LiH | BeH$_2$ | BH$_3$ | CH$_4$ | NH$_3$ | OH$_2$ | FH |
|---|---|---|---|---|---|---|
| basic | | | neutral | weak base | neutral | acidic |
| ionic | | covalent | covalent molecules | polar covalent | | |

| NaH | MgH$_2$ | AlH$_3$ | SiH$_4$ | PH$_3$ | SH$_2$ | ClH |
|---|---|---|---|---|---|---|
| basic | | | neutral | very weak base | weak acid | acid |
| ionic | | covalent | covalent molecules | covalent | covalent | polar covalent |

## 6.8 Alkali metals

The alkali metals is the name given to the elements in group I i.e. lithium, sodium, potassium, rubidium, caesium and francium.

**Physical properties**    The alkali metals show **metallic behaviour** to a high degree. They are soft and can be cut with a knife to show the typical metallic lustre. They are malleable, and they are good conductors of heat and electricity.

Table 6.2 gives some information about the properties of the alkali metals.

**Table 6.2**

| Alkali metal | Density g cm$^{-3}$ | m.p. K | b.p. K | Ionic radius nm | Ionization energy kJ mol$^{-1}$ |
|---|---|---|---|---|---|
| lithium | 0.53 | 453 | 1590 | 0.068 | 520 |
| sodium | 0.97 | 371 | 1156 | 0.097 | 496 |
| potassium | 0.86 | 337 | 1047 | 0.133 | 419 |
| rubidium | 1.53 | 312 | 961 | 0.147 | 403 |
| caesium | 1.87 | 301 | 951 | 0.167 | 376 |

*Note:* 1 nm = $10^{-9}$ m

**The densities** of lithium, sodium and potassium are less than that of water (1.00 g cm$^{-3}$) so these metals float on the surface of water. The relatively low densities suggests that the atoms of the alkali metals are not closely packed. The increasing density as we go down the group suggests that the metals become more closely packed as the nuclear charge increases.

The **ionic radii** of the alkali metals increase as we go down the group. This is due to the increasing number of energy levels.

| Alkali metal | Electron arrangement |
|---|---|
| lithium | 2.1 |
| sodium | 2.8.1 |
| potassium | 2.8.8.1 |
| rubidium | 2.8.18.8.1 |
| caesium | 2.8.18.18.8.1 |

The **ionization energy** of the alkali metals decreases as we go down the group. This is due to the increased size of the atoms which results in a decreased attraction for the valency electrons despite the increased nuclear charge. As far as ionization energies go, the values for the alkali metals are relatively low indicating that it is fairly easy to pull the single valency electron off a neutral atom.

The amount of energy required to pull a second electron off the alkali metal is extremely high.

The **melting points** of the alkali metals are relatively low, and in this respect they are not like many of the other metals. The low melting points can be accounted for if we consider the structure of metallic sodium. Sodium metal crystallizes in a body-centred cubic lattice in which the lattice points are occupied by 1+ ions and the valency electrons permeate the whole lattice.

The charged nucleus of an atom attracts the electrons of its neighbours and these forces of attraction hold the crystal lattice together. The valency electrons however, are far enough away from the nucleus to become de-localized and free to move through the bulk of the material. Since the alkali metals are soft we can deduce that the metallic bond is weak and it also follows that the structure is not close-packed, which accounts for the low densities. Iron for example, has exactly the same type of metallic bonding, but it is very hard and dense and we deduce that the bonding is strong. To melt the metal we require to supply enough energy to break the stronger metallic bonding and this explains why the alkali metals melt more easily than iron.

The melting points decrease as we go down the group due to the increased size of the atoms and the resulting smaller attraction for the electrons.

**Occurrence and extraction**

The alkali metals occur in nature as the $1+$ ions. Since most of the compounds of the alkali metals are soluble in water, they are found in sea water and also in large salt deposits formed when seas evaporated millions of years ago. To extract the alkali metals, the $1+$ ion has to be reduced.

$$Na^+ + e^- \rightarrow Na$$

**Table 6.3**

| Alkali metal | Reaction | $E°$ V |
|---|---|---|
| lithium | $Li^+ + e^- \rightarrow Li$ | $-3.05$ |
| sodium | $Na^+ + e^- \rightarrow Na$ | $-2.71$ |
| potassium | $K^+ + e^- \rightarrow K$ | $-2.92$ |
| rubidium | $Rb^+ + e^- \rightarrow Rb$ | $-2.93$ |
| caesium | $Cs^+ + e^- \rightarrow Cs$ | $-2.92$ |

The high negative values indicate that the reactions do not proceed easily i.e. the alkali metal ions are not easy to reduce. The alkali metals cannot be reduced easily by chemical means, and the normal method of extraction is by electrolysis of the fused salts. Figure 6.15 shows the Downs' Cell which is used in the extraction of sodium from molten sodium chloride.

**Figure 6.15** The Downs' cell

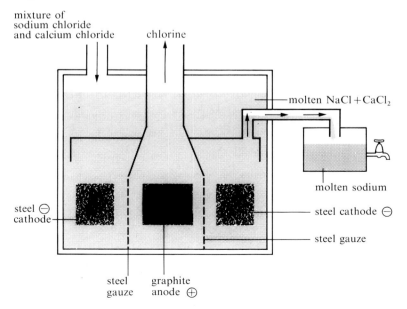

The reactions are:

$$Na^+ + e^- \rightarrow Na \qquad \text{at the cathode}$$
$$2Cl^- \rightarrow Cl_2 + 2e^- \qquad \text{at the anode}$$

The products have to be kept apart to prevent them from reacting.

If we look again at Tables 6.2 and 6.3 there would appear to be a discrepancy in the behaviour of lithium. Table 6.2 indicates that lithium holds onto its electron more tightly than the other alkali metals, yet Table 6.3 indicates that the lithium ion is the most difficult to reduce, or the lithium atom is the most easy to oxidize. The explanation is the fact that the ionization energy is a property of an isolated atom, whereas the $E^\circ$ value is the result of three consecutive steps, each involving energy changes.

$$Li(s) \rightarrow Li(g) \qquad (1)$$
$$Li(g) \rightarrow Li(g)^+ + e^- \qquad (2)$$
$$Li(g)^+ + H_2O \rightarrow Li(aq)^+ \qquad (3)$$

Step (1) corresponds to the sublimation energy which is approximately the same for all the alkali metals.

Step (2) corresponds to the ionization energy, which is highest for lithium.

Step (3) corresponds to the hydration energy which is the energy given out when the gaseous metal ion goes into solution. The hydration energy for the lithium ion is so great that it more than makes up for the higher ionization energy of the lithium atom. The hydration energy for the lithium ion is much greater than the hydration energy for the other alkali metal ions because the lithium ion is extremely small and the water has a great stabilizing effect on it.

**Chemical properties**

As we can see from their high $E^\circ$ values, the alkali metals are extremely good reducing agents. In fact they are the most reactive metals known, and this causes special problems in their handling and storage. To prevent the alkali metals from reacting with the moisture in the air, they are stored under liquid paraffin.

The reaction with water is violent and involves the evolution of hydrogen gas.

$$2Na(s) + 2H_2O(l) \rightarrow 2NaOH(aq) + H_2(g)$$

The reaction with oxygen in the air leads to the formation of oxides. The alkali metals also combine directly with the halogens and sulphur.

$$2Na(s) + Cl_2(g) \rightarrow 2NaCl(s)$$
$$2Na(s) + S(s) \rightarrow Na_2S(s)$$

**Sodium hydroxide**

One of the most important alkali metal compounds is sodium hydroxide. It is manufactured by the electrolysis of brine using a mercury cathode. Sodium is liberated at the cathode and forms a sodium-mercury amalgam.

$$Na^+(aq) + e^- \rightarrow Na/Hg(l)$$

Chlorine is liberated at the anode.

$$2Cl^-(aq) \rightarrow Cl_2(g) + 2e^-$$

The sodium-mercury amalgam reacts with water to produce sodium hydroxide.

$$2Na/Hg(l) + 2H_2O(l) \rightarrow 2NaOH(aq) + H_2(g) + 2Hg(l)$$

Figure 6.16 shows a suitable cell for the electrolysis.

**Figure 6.16**

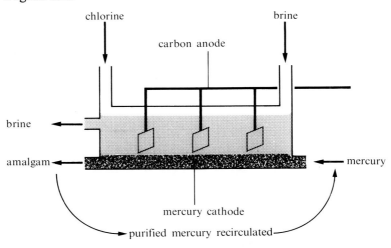

Sodium hydroxide is a strong alkali, being fully ionized in aqueous solution.

$$Na^+OH^-(s) + H_2O \rightarrow Na^+(aq) + OH^-(aq)$$

Sodium hydroxide is used in large quantities in industry in petroleum refining, paper-making and the manufacture of soaps and soapless detergents.

**Sodium chloride**    Sodium chloride is common salt. It occurs naturally as rock salt and also in sea water, but it can be prepared by direct combination of the elements. It is worthwhile looking at the energy changes in the formation of sodium chloride, from its elements.

First consider the endothermic steps.

$$\frac{1}{2}Cl_2(g) \rightarrow Cl(g) \qquad \Delta H = +120\,kJ$$

$$Na(s) \rightarrow Na(g) \qquad \Delta H = +109\,kJ$$

$$Na(g) \rightarrow Na^+(g) + e^- \qquad \Delta H = +496\,kJ$$

$$\Delta H = +725\,kJ$$

Now consider the exothermic steps.

$$Cl(g) + e^- \rightarrow Cl^-(g) \qquad \Delta H = -362\,kJ$$

$$Na^+(g) + Cl^-(g) \rightarrow Na^+Cl^-(s) \qquad \Delta H = -781\,kJ$$

$$\Delta H = -1143\,kJ$$

The heat given out is much greater than the heat taken in. Therefore we might expect the product to be more stable than the reactants.

The largest factor in the energy considerations is formation of solid sodium chloride from the gaseous ions. It is the **lattice energy**.

**Lattice structures**    Sodium chloride forms a simple cubic lattice in which the lattice points are occupied by alternate sodium ions and chloride ions.

**Figure 6.17**

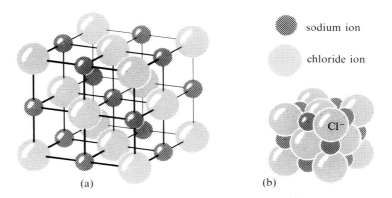

(a)                                    (b)

If we look at a section of this lattice, shown on the right, we see that each sodium ion is surrounded by six chloride ions. Lithium chloride, sodium bromide, potassium chloride and many other compounds have a similar lattice pattern.

Caesium chloride also forms a simple cubic lattice, but in this case the arrangement is not quite the same.

**Figure 6.18**

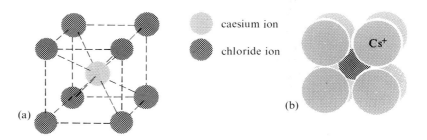

(a)                                    (b)

If we look at a section of this lattice, shown on the right, we see that each caesium ion is surrounded by eight chloride ions. In the same way, each chloride ion is surrounded by eight caesium ions. This packing is possible because the caesium ion is larger and allows more anions to pack round it. The critical ratio of cation radius to anion radius to allow eight ions to pack around in this way is 0.8. If the ratio is less than 0.8, then only six ions can pack round.

### 6.9 The halogens

This is the name given to the group VII elements, i.e. fluorine, chlorine, bromine, iodine.

**Physical properties** The halogens exhibit typical non-metal characteristics existing as covalently bonded diatomic molecules.

Table 6.4 gives some information about the properties of the halogens.

**Table 6.4**

| Halogen | m.p. K | b.p. K | Ionic radius nm | Ionization energy kJ mol$^{-1}$ | Covalent radius nm |
|---------|------|------|-------|------------|-------|
| fluorine | 53 | 85 | 0.133 | 1681 | 0.072 |
| chlorine | 172 | 238 | 0.181 | 1255 | 0.099 |
| bromine | 266 | 332 | 0.196 | 1142 | 0.114 |
| iodine | 387 | 457 | 0.220 | 1009 | 0.133 |

The halogen family is a good example of the gradation in properties that occurs when moving down a group of the Periodic Table. If we compare their **melting points** and **boiling points**, we see that fluorine and chlorine are gases, bromine is a volatile liquid and iodine is a volatile solid. The gradation in melting point and boiling point can be accounted for by examining the relative sizes of the covalent molecules. We can see from Table 6.4 that the melting points and boiling points of the halogens increase as the covalent radii of the molecules increase. This is because the larger molecules have more electrons in their structure which give rise to greater Van der Waals' forces between the molecules.

The melting points and boiling points of the halogens are relatively low when compared with those of other elements. This is because Van der Waals' forces are weak in comparison with other types of inter- and intra-molecular attractions.

The **ionic radii and covalent radii** of the halogens increase as we go down the group due to the increasing number of energy levels.

| Halogen | Electron arrangement |
|---------|---------------------|
| fluorine | 2.7 |
| chlorine | 2.8.7 |
| bromine | 2.8.18.7 |
| iodine | 2.8.18.18.7 |
| astatine | 2.8.18.32.18.7 |

The **ionization energies** of the halogens are relatively high showing it is difficult to remove an outer electron from the atom. Removal of an electron from fluorine is the most difficult because the fluorine atom is so small that the outer electrons are very close to the nucleus. Removal of an outer electron from iodine is the least difficult because iodine is a larger atom and the outer electrons are farther from the nucleus which is attracting them.

When we compare **electron affinity values** in Table 6.1 we find that the halogen group shows a decreasing affinity for electrons as we move down the group. As we found in the alkali metals, the size of the atom is a more dominant factor than the nuclear charge in determining the attraction for outer electrons.

**Occurrence and extraction**
The halogens occur in nature as negative ions in sea water and as salt deposits from dried-up seas.

Table 6.5 gives the $E^\circ$ values for the halogens.

**Table 6.5**

| Halogen | Reaction | $E^\circ$ V |
|---|---|---|
| fluorine | $\frac{1}{2}F_2 + e^- \rightarrow F^-$ | +2.87 |
| chlorine | $\frac{1}{2}Cl_2 + e^- \rightarrow Cl^-$ | +1.36 |
| bromine | $\frac{1}{2}Br_2 + e^- \rightarrow Br^-$ | +1.07 |
| iodine | $\frac{1}{2}I_2 + e^- \rightarrow I^-$ | +0.54 |

We can see from the positive values that these reactions tend to go in the direction indicated, i.e. the natural tendency is for the halogens to exist as halide ions. This tendency has to be reversed when extracting the halogens, and the usual procedure is by electrolysis of the aqueous solutions of the halides. This does not work for fluorine, because of its strong tendency to exist as the fluoride ion. To extract fluorine the molten salt must be electrolysed.

**Chemical properties**
The halogens are all oxidizing agents as shown by their positive $E^\circ$ values. Their relative strengths diminish as we go down the group and correspondingly the stability of the ion formed diminishes as we go down the group.

| | | | |
|---|---|---|---|
| $F_2$ | good oxidizing agent | $F^-$ | poor reducing agent |
| $Cl_2$ | good oxidizing agent | $Cl^-$ | poor reducing agent |
| $Br_2$ | mild oxidizing agent | $Br^-$ | mild reducing agent |
| $I_2$ | poor oxidizing agent | $I^-$ | strong reducing agent |

The halogens will therefore displace each other from their salts depending on their relative strengths as oxidizing agents.

If chlorine water is added to a solution of potassium bromide, the yellow-red colour of bromine appears.

$$Cl_2(aq) + 2e^- \rightarrow 2Cl^-(aq) \qquad \text{reduction}$$
$$2Br^-(aq) \rightarrow Br_2(aq) + 2e^- \qquad \text{oxidation}$$

$$Cl_2(aq) + 2Br^-(aq) \rightarrow 2Cl^-(aq) + Br_2(aq) \quad \text{redox}$$

If bromine water is added to a solution of potassium iodide the iodine is displaced either as a yellow colour or as a black solid depending on the concentrations.

$$Br_2(aq) + 2e^- \rightarrow 2Br^- \qquad \text{reduction}$$
$$2I^-(aq) \rightarrow I_2(aq) + 2e^- \qquad \text{oxidation}$$

$$Br_2(aq) + 2I^-(aq) \rightarrow 2Br^-(aq) + I_2(aq) \quad \text{redox}$$

These reactions are sometimes used as tests for halides in solution. However, the precipitates formed with silver(I) nitrate are the more well-known tests for halides.

Tests for halides    If silver(I) nitrate solution is added to a halide solution, the silver(I) halides precipitate. Each has a characteristic colour.

$$Cl^-(aq) + Ag^+(aq) \rightarrow AgCl(s)$$
white

$$Br^-(aq) + Ag^+(aq) \rightarrow AgBr(s)$$
pale yellow

$$I^-(aq) + Ag^+(aq) \rightarrow AgI(s)$$
yellow

The halogens combine directly with hydrogen to form the hydrogen halides. Hydrogen fluoride and hydrogen chloride can be prepared by the action of concentrated sulphuric acid on the appropriate salt, provided special precautions are taken with the apparatus in the case of hydrogen fluoride.

$$NaCl + H_2SO_4 \rightarrow NaHSO_4 + HCl$$

$$NaF + H_2SO_4 \rightarrow NaHSO_4 + HF$$

However, if the same reactions are tried with a bromide or an iodide, we find that the ions are strong enough reducing agents to reduce the sulphuric acid to sulphur dioxide and hydrogen sulphide respectively.

$$2NaBr + 2H_2SO_4 \rightarrow SO_2 + Br_2 + Na_2SO_4 + 2H_2O$$

$$8NaI + 5H_2SO_4 \rightarrow H_2S + 4I_2 + 4Na_2SO_4 + 4H_2O$$

This serves to illustrate the reducing properties of the halides, but in order to prepare them, we require to use an acid which is not as strong an oxidizing agent as sulphuric acid. Such an acid is phosphoric acid.

$$6NaBr(s) + 2H_3PO_4(l) \rightarrow 2Na_3PO_4(aq) + 6HBr(g)$$

$$6NaI(s) + 2H_3PO_4(l) \rightarrow 2Na_3PO_4(aq) + 6HI(g)$$

The halogens combine directly with metals to form metal halides.

$$2Na(s) + Cl_2(g) \rightarrow 2NaCl(s)$$

$$Cu(s) + Cl_2(g) \rightarrow CuCl_2(s)$$

$$2Na(s) + Br_2(l) \rightarrow 2NaBr(s)$$

The bonding in metal halides is usually ionic and this is what would be expected when the differences in electronegativities are compared.
The bonding in hydrogen halides is polar covalent and they all dissolve in water to give acid solution.

**Summary**

From this chapter you should know:

1   How the elements are arranged in the Periodic Table.

2   The physical properties of elements form a pattern in the Periodic Table.

3   How the properties of chlorides, oxides and hydrides vary from group to group.

4   Some of the properties of the alkali metals.

5   Some of the properties of the halogens.

**Questions**

1

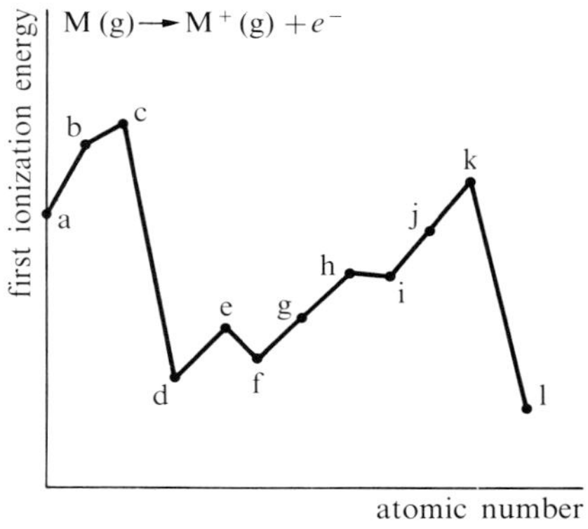

The diagram shows part of a graph of first **ionization energy** (the energy required to remove one electron from an element in its gaseous state) against atomic number, but it is not known at which element this part of the graph starts.

Which of the elements can be identified as members of:

    **1.1**   The halogens?

    **1.2**   The alkali metals?

    **1.3**   The noble (inert) gases?

**2**   Suggest an explanation of the fact that the ionization energies of the alkali metals decrease as atomic number increases.

**3**   Starting with lithium metal and any other chemicals required, outline how you could prepare lithium chloride:

    **3.1**   By direct synthesis.

    **3.2**   By a reaction scheme involving neutralization.

Write balanced equations for any chemical reactions involved.

**4**   How could chlorine be obtained from lithium chloride?

(Experimental details are not required.) *SCEEB*

**2**  **1**  The formulae of the simplest compounds of chlorine with sodium, carbon, and phosphorus are NaCl, $CCl_4$, and $PCl_3$. Draw up a table similar to that shown below and state in it how these compounds vary in respect of:

    **1.1**  Physical state under laboratory conditions
    **1.2**  Main type of bonding
    **1.3**  Behaviour on addition of water.

| | Physical state | Bonding | Action of water |
|---|---|---|---|
| NaCl | | | |
| $CCl_4$ | | | |
| $PCl_3$ | | | |

Show how the physical state of these compounds is related to bonding.

**2**  One method of preparing the hydrogen halides is to react the corresponding sodium halide with concentrated sulphuric acid. It is found that this works well in the case of sodium fluoride and sodium chloride, but that with sodium bromide and sodium iodide the halogen element is obtained as well as the hydrogen halide. Suggest a reason why this happens.

**3**  From your knowledge of the chlorides of phosphorus state how phosphorus tribromide or phosphorus pentabromide might be obtained. What gas would be evolved when water acts on either of these compounds? Suggest a method by which hydrogen bromide could be obtained from a mixture of the gas with bromine vapour. *SCEEB*

**3**

| Substance | Melting point (K) | Boiling point (K) | Electrical conductivity of solid | Electrical conductivity of melt |
|---|---|---|---|---|
| A | 365 | 463 | nil | nil |
| B | 1323 | 2773 | good | good |
| C | 1046 | 1680 | nil | good |
| D | 2156 | 2776 | nil | nil |

Place A, B, C, and D in the appropriate categories from the following:
(a) Metallic solid    (b) Covalent network solid
(c) Ionic solid    (d) Covalent molecular solid. *SCEEB*

**4**  Write an essay on 'Forces of attraction in chemistry'. In your answer you should refer to the following topics:

Covalent bonding (large and small structures).
Ionic (electrovalent) bonding.
Intermediate cases of the above.
Comparison of forces to be overcome in melting compounds containing these bonds.
Hydrogen bonding.
Metallic bonding.

Your answer should be illustrated by examples. *SCEEB*

5    Write an essay on 'Elements 1 to 20 in the Periodic Table'.
In your answer you should refer to the following topics:

Metals and non-metals.
Electronic configuration.
Structure and bonding.
Vertical and horizontal trends in properties (e.g. ionization energy,
electronegativity).
Trends in structures and properties of oxides, hydrides, and chlorides of the
elements. *SCEEB*

6    **1**    The following graph illustrates the trends in the boiling points for the
group 4 hydrides. Explain this trend.

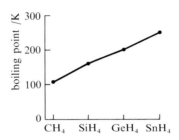

**2**    Using the values below, sketch a similar graph for the group 6 hydrides.

| *Hydride* | *Boiling point* (K) |
|-----------|---------------------|
| $H_2O$    | 373                 |
| $H_2S$    | 213                 |
| $H_2Se$   | 231                 |
| $H_2Te$   | 271                 |

**3**    Offer an explanation for the difference in the shape of the graphs in
**1** and **2**.
**4**    What other properties of the group 6 hydrides will show a similar
trend? *P & W*

7    Explain why:
    **1.1**    A sodium atom is larger than a magnesium atom.
    **1.2**    A potassium atom is larger than a sodium atom.
    **2**

|           | *Ionization energy* (kJ mole$^{-1}$) | |
|-----------|--------|--------|
| *Element* | *1st*  | *2nd*  |
| Sodium    | 494    | 4560   |
| Magnesium | 736    | 1450   |

Explain why:

**2.1**    Second ionization energies are greater than first ionization energies.

**2.2**    The difference between the first and second ionization energies is much greater for sodium than for magnesium.

3    Suggest explanations for the variation in the melting points of the following compounds by relating the nature of bonding to the position of the elements in the Periodic Table.

| Compound | Melting point (K) |
| --- | --- |
| Hydrogen chloride | 159 |
| Hydrogen fluoride | 190 |
| Methane | 90.5 |
| Sodium hydride | 1073 |

*P & W*

# 7 Chemical reaction and equilibrium

### 7.1 The same rate?

1  When 20 cm³ of 1M hydrochloric acid are added to 20 cm³ of 1M sodium hydroxide, the resulting solution becomes neutral immediately.
2  When zinc is added to dilute hydrochloric acid, we can see the reaction taking place, as hydrogen gas is produced, but it takes some time before the reaction stops.
3  When iron comes in contact with oxygen and moisture, it rusts, but it is a gradual process and it can take years before all the iron rusts.

These examples show that reactions take place at different rates. The rate of a chemical reaction is the speed at which the products are formed.

### 7.2 Collision theory

Before a chemical reaction can take place, it is assumed that there must be collisions between the reacting species. Consider the reaction:

$$A + B \rightarrow C + D$$

The reactants A and B must collide with each other before the products C and D are produced.

### 7.3 The minimum energy

For a chemical reaction to occur, a collision is necessary. However, a mixture of hydrogen gas and oxygen gas will remain inert without any tendency to combine, although when 1 mole of each gas is mixed, the number of collisions may be as high as $10^{30}$ per second. Obviously the collision theory is not a complete explanation.

The molecules of a gas at any one time are in random motion and possess widely differing kinetic energies. The distribution of kinetic energy is nearly a normal distribution, as shown in Figure 7.1.

**Figure 7.1** The distribution of kinetic energies in molecules

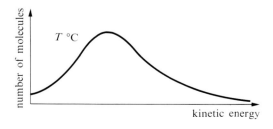

We can assume that molecules must possess a certain minimum energy before they will react on collision. If we consider the distribution of energy amongst the molecules in terms of a normal distribution, we shall find that only a small number of the molecules have sufficient kinetic energy $E$ for reaction. If the temperature is raised by 10 °C, then more molecules will have the required energy for reaction (Figure 7.2).

**Figure 7.2**

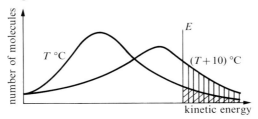

An increase in temperature causes an increase in the rate of reaction.

### 7.4 Activation energy and activated complexes

All molecules and atoms possess a certain amount of potential energy due to the forces of attraction and repulsion associated with them. Consider two molecules approaching each other. They both possess kinetic energy, but, because the electron clouds repel each other, they will slow down and some of the kinetic energy will be changed into potential energy. If the collision is ineffective, then the molecules will separate and some of the potential energy will be changed into kinetic energy. If the collision is effective, then the kinetic energy will be converted into potential energy and an **activated complex** will be formed. Consider the reaction:

$$A + B \rightleftharpoons C + D$$

When A and B react to form an activated complex, a certain minimum energy is required. This is called the **activation energy**. The activated complex may either break up to re-form the reactants or break up to form the products.

$$A + B \rightleftharpoons X \rightleftharpoons C + D$$

When the complex breaks up to form the products, the energy given out may be more or less than the activation energy. From Figure 7.3 we can see that the energy associated with the reactants is greater than the energy associated with the products. During the reaction there will be a release of energy, and so the reaction is exothermic.

**Figure 7.3**

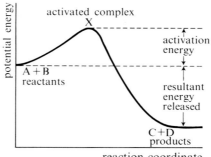

If the energy associated with the products is greater than that associated with the reactants, there will be an overall intake of energy, and so the reaction will be endothermic (Figure 7.4).

**Figure 7.4**

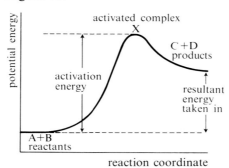

The effect of temperature upon reaction rates can be explained by saying that an increase in temperature increases the number of particles which can provide the necessary activation energy, and so the rate increases.

### 7.5 Collision geometry

We must consider how the activated complex forms. The way in which the molecules collide will determine whether or not the complex will form. Consider the reaction:

$$X_2 + Y_2 \rightleftharpoons 2XY$$

If the molecules collide side on, there is a possibility of forming a complex,

| X | | Y | | X----Y | | X——Y |
|---|---|---|---|---|---|---|
| \| | + | \| | $\rightleftharpoons$ | : : | $\rightleftharpoons$ | + |
| X | | Y | | X----Y | | X——Y |
| Reactants | | | | Activated complex | | Products |

which would then form the products. If the molecules collide end on there is no possibility of the activated complex forming:

$$X—X + Y—Y \rightarrow \text{no reaction}$$

### 7.6  Action of catalysts

A catalyst is a substance which changes the speed of a reaction without itself being chemically changed or used up. The function of a catalyst is usually to allow a different reaction mechanism to occur. The catalyst provides alternative steps which involve lower activation energies. Let us consider again the reaction:

$$X_2 + Y_2 \rightarrow 2XY$$

The suggested mechanism without a catalyst is:

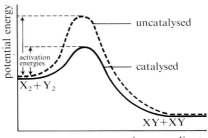

When a catalyst Z is used, the activation energy is lowered and a possible explanation for this could be that a different activated complex with a lower activation energy is formed. The suggested mechanism with a catalyst is:

**Figure 7.5**

The effect of the catalyst is shown in Figure 7.5. The activation energy for the catalysed reaction is lower than that of the uncatalysed reaction. As a result, the reaction will proceed more easily in the presence of the catalyst.


### 7.7  Factors affecting the rate of reaction

**Particle size**  If equal weights of powdered chalk and lump chalk are added to equal volumes of 1M hydrochloric acid, the reaction involving the powdered chalk is almost instantaneous, while that with the lump chalk takes some time. This result indicates that the rate of reaction depends on particle size, the smaller the particles the faster the reaction. For equal masses of small and large particles, the small particles have a greater total surface area and thus there is a greater opportunity for collisions to occur.

**Concentration** Since a reaction depends on the number of effective collisions, we can assume that an increase in concentration will increase the rate of reaction. We shall consider the reaction between sodium thiosulphate and hydrochloric acid.

$$S_2O_3^{2-}(aq) + 2H^+(aq) \rightarrow H_2O(l) + SO_2(g) + S(s)$$

As you can see from the equation, one of the products is sulphur, and we can use the appearance of the precipitate to determine the rate of the reaction. Different volumes of 0.1M sodium thiosulphate solution are placed in conical flasks and 5 cm³ of 1M hydrochloric acid are added to each flask. A cross is marked on a piece of paper and the flasks are held over the cross. The time taken for the cross to be obscured by the precipitate is noted in each case. Table 7.1 shows a typical set of results.

**Table 7.1**

| Volume of 0.1 M sodium thiosulphate added (cm³) | Volume of water added (cm³) | Relative concentration of sodium thiosulphate | Time t for cross to be obscured (s) | Rate $\frac{1}{t}(s^{-1}) \times 10^3$ |
|---|---|---|---|---|
| 100 | 0 | 5 | 99 | 10.1 |
| 80 | 20 | 4 | 125 | 8.0 |
| 60 | 40 | 3 | 161 | 6.2 |
| 40 | 60 | 2 | 250 | 4.0 |
| 20 | 80 | 1 | 500 | 2.0 |

**Figure 7.6**

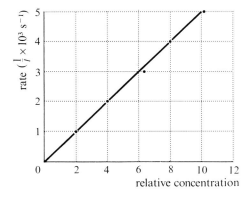

If a graph of relative concentration against rate is plotted, the line in Figure 7.6 is obtained. We can see from the graph that an increase in the concentration increases the rate of the reaction.

**Temperature** As the temperature of a substance is raised, so the energy of the particles in the substance will increase. This increase in energy will cause the particles to move more quickly. This increases the possibility of effective collisions, and thus causes an increase in the reaction rate. Let us consider again the reaction between hydrochloric acid and sodium thiosulphate solution.

$$Na_2S_2O_3(aq) + 2HCl(aq) \rightarrow H_2O(l) + SO_2(g) + S(s) + 2NaCl(aq)$$

The appearance of the colloidal precipitate of sulphur can again be used to determine the reaction rate. 100 cm³ of 0.25M sodium thiosulphate solution are placed in a beaker together with 100 cm³ of water, and the beaker is heated until a suitable temperature is reached. 10 cm³ of 1M hydrochloric acid are added to the sodium thiosulphate solution and the time taken for a cross to be obscured by the precipitate of sulphur is noted. The experiment is repeated over a range of temperatures. Table 7.2 shows a typical set of results.

**Table 7.2**

| Temperature (°C) | Time $t$ (s) | Rate $\frac{1}{t}$ (s⁻¹) × 10³ |
|---|---|---|
| 19 | 40 | 25 |
| 25 | 29 | 34 |
| 33 | 19 | 53 |
| 38 | 15 | 67 |
| 45 | 10 | 100 |
| 56 | 7 | 143 |
| 59 | 6 | 167 |

A graph of the reaction rate plotted against the temperature is shown in Figure 7.7. As you can see from the graph, the rate of reaction increases as the temperature increases.

**Figure 7.7** Effect of temperature on the rate of reaction

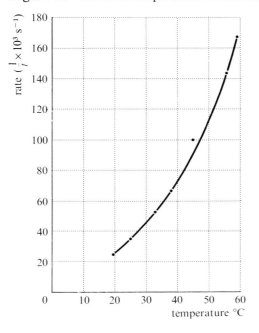

**Light**

In the absence of light bromine will react very slowly with hexane to form bromohexane.

$$C_6H_{14}(l) + Br_2(\text{dissolved in } CCl_4) \rightarrow C_6H_{13}Br(l) + HBr(g)$$

If, however, the reaction is carried out in sunlight, substitution occurs in a very short time. The light provides the necessary energy of activation for the reaction.

Photosynthesis is an example of a photochemical reaction.

$$6CO_2(g) + 6H_2O(l) + \text{energy} \xrightarrow{\text{chlorophyll}} C_6H_{12}O_6 + 6O_2$$
$$\text{glucose}$$
$$nC_6H_{12}O_6 \longrightarrow (C_6H_{10}O_5)_n + nH_2O$$
$$\text{starch}$$

photosynthesis

The sunlight provides the necessary activation energy.

**Chain reactions**

### Chlorine and methane

Methane and chlorine do not react in the dark at room temperature, however if the mixture is exposed to ultra-violet light (or sunlight), the chlorine molecule breaks down to form two chlorine atoms. (Note: an atom which has an unpaired electron, like $Cl\cdot$, is known as a free radical).

$$Cl_2 \xrightarrow{\text{u.v. light}} Cl\cdot + Cl\cdot$$

A chlorine radical reacts with a molecule of methane

$$Cl\cdot + CH_4 \longrightarrow CH_3\cdot + HCl$$

The methyl radical reacts with another molecule of chlorine

$$CH_3\cdot + Cl_2 \longrightarrow CH_3Cl + Cl\cdot$$

The chlorine radical starts the process again by reacting with another molecule of methane, hence we have a chain reaction.

*Safety note.* Chain reactions are often explosive and special precautions must be observed when they are demonstrated.

### Chlorine and hydrogen

Chlorine gas and hydrogen gas are mixed together and the mixture is exposed to ultra-violet light (or sunlight). The chlorine molecules dissociate into chlorine radicals.

$$Cl_2 \xrightarrow{\text{u.v. light}} Cl\cdot + Cl\cdot$$

The chlorine radical reacts with a molecule of hydrogen

$$Cl\cdot + H_2 \longrightarrow HCl + H\cdot$$

The hydrogen radical reacts with another molecule of chlorine

$$H\cdot + Cl_2 \longrightarrow HCl + Cl\cdot$$

The chlorine radical has been regenerated and the reaction begins again.

**Reaction mechanism**

The mechanism for the reaction
$$H_2O_2 + 2HI \rightarrow 2H_2O + I_2$$
is

(a)  $H_2O_2 + I^- \rightarrow HIO + OH^-$  (slow)
(b)  $H^+ + OH^- \rightarrow H_2O$  (fast)
(c)  $HIO + H^+ + I^- \rightarrow H_2O + I_2$  (fast)

The rate of the overall reaction is determined by the rate of reaction (a), which is called the **rate determining step.**

**Catalysts**

If hydrogen peroxide is allowed to stand, it will gradually decompose to form water and oxygen gas

$$2H_2O_2(l) \rightarrow 2H_2O(l) + O_2(g)$$

However, if some manganese dioxide is added, the reaction is almost instantaneous. The manganese dioxide, the catalyst, can be recovered unchanged at the end of the experiment.

**Conclusion**

Chemical reactions can be affected by particle size, pressure, concentration, temperature, light and catalysts.

### 7.8 Equilibrium

We have studied a number of equilibrium reactions and we now know that this type of reaction is fairly common.

In the contact process:

$$2SO_2(g) + O_2(g) \rightleftharpoons 2SO_3(s)$$

In the Haber process:

$$N_2(g) + 3H_2(g) \rightleftharpoons 2NH_3(g)$$

Equilibrium reactions are dynamic in nature as there is a continual interchange of atoms between reactants and products. Consider the equation:

$$A + B \rightleftharpoons C + D$$

From the previous sections we know that the rate of reaction depends on temperature. We also know that there are two reactions taking place:

Forward reaction    $A + B \rightarrow C + D$

Reverse reaction    $C + D \rightarrow A + B$

The rate of the forward reaction ($R_1$) is proportional to ($\propto$) the concentration of A, denoted by [A], multiplied by the concentration of B, denoted by [B].

rate of forward reaction $\propto$ concentration A $\times$ concentration B

$$R_1 \propto [A][B]$$

$$R_1 = k_1[A][B] \text{ where } k_1 \text{ is a constant}$$

Similarly rate of reverse reaction $\propto$ concentration C $\times$ concentration D

$$R_2 \propto [C][D]$$
$$R_2 = k_2[C][D] \text{ where } k_2 \text{ is a constant.}$$

At equilibrium, the rate of forward reaction equals the rate of reverse reaction.

$$\text{i.e. } R_1 = R_2$$
$$\text{or } k_1[A][B] = k_2[C][D]$$
$$\frac{k_1}{k_2} = \frac{[C][D]}{[A][B]} = K.$$

$K$ is known as the equilibrium constant and is a constant for any particular reaction at any particular temperature.

A reaction is said to be at equilibrium when the two opposing rates become equal. Any factor which affects the rate of one or other of these reactions may affect the equilibrium position, for example, concentration, pressure, or temperature.

We have suggested that a catalyst provides an alternative reaction path with a lower activation energy. The activation energy of both the forward and reverse reactions are lowered by identical amounts. Therefore there will be no net change in the equilibrium position, although the use of a catalyst means that the system will reach equilibrium much more quickly.

### 7.9 Le Chatelier's principle

Le Chatelier's principle states that, if the conditions of a system in equilibrium are altered, the system will attempt to reduce the effects of the imposed conditions. We can use Le Chatelier's principle to account for the effects of changes in concentration, pressure, and temperature upon a system at equilibrium.

**Concentration**  Consider the system:

$$NH_3(g) + H_2O(l) \rightleftharpoons NH_4^+(aq) + OH^-(aq)$$

Sufficient ammonia solution is added to 100 cm³ of water to give a pH of about 12. Solid ammonium chloride is added to the solution. The concentration of the $NH_4^+$ ions on the right-hand side is increased. The pH of the solution drops, showing that the increase in concentration has caused the reaction to move towards the left and has reduced the concentration of the $OH^-$ ions on the right-hand side. Le Chatelier's principle applies to all changes of concentration. If the concentration of the reactants or products in a system at equilibrium is altered, then the system will act to reduce the effect of this increase in concentration.

**Temperature**  In general, an increase in temperature favours a reaction which is an endothermic process and a decrease in temperature favours a reaction which is an exothermic process. Consider the equilibrium betweeen dinitrogen tetroxide and nitrogen dioxide:

$$N_2O_4(g) \rightleftharpoons 2NO_2(g) \qquad \Delta H = +58 \text{ kJ}$$
yellow           dark brown

A mixture of $NO_2/N_2O_4$ is placed in each of three separate density bottles. One bottle is placed in water at 25 °C, one is placed in water at 50 °C and one is placed in boiling water. After some time the colours in the bottles can be compared (Figure 7.8).

**Figure 7.8**

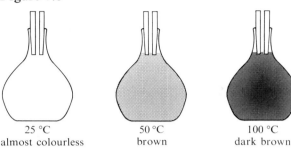

| 25 °C | 50 °C | 100 °C |
| almost colourless | brown | dark brown |

From Figure 7.8 we can see that as the temperature increases, more nitrogen dioxide is produced and this is what we would expect since the reaction is endothermic.

**Pressure**    Pressure is the result of gas molecules bombarding the walls of the vessel in which the gas is contained. Obviously the greater the number of molecules in a given volume, the greater the pressure will be. Consider the system:

$$N_2O_4(g) \rightleftharpoons 2NO_2(g)$$

Effectively, the pressure on the right-hand side is greater than that on the left-hand side because there are more molecules on the right-hand side. The formation of nitrogen dioxide is accompanied by an increase in pressure. A reduction in the pressure on the system would result in the equilibrium moving to the right, which, according to the equation, would cause a pressure increase and this would help to minimize the overall reduction of pressure on the system.

### 7.10 Equilibrium in practice

**(a) Contact Process**    Over 90 per cent of the sulphuric acid manufactured in the United Kingdom is made by the contact process. The starting point in the process is sulphur dioxide, obtained by burning sulphur in air.

$$S(s) + O_2(g) \rightarrow SO_2(g)$$

The sulphur dioxide is purified and reacted with the oxygen of the air in the presence of a vanadium(V) oxide catalyst.

$$2SO_2(g) + O_2(g) \overset{V_2O_5}{\rightleftharpoons} 2SO_3(g)$$

This is a reversible reaction and we can apply Le Chatelier's principle to it.

**Effect of pressure**    $2SO_2(g) + O_2(g) \rightleftharpoons 2SO_3(g)$
2 moles    1 mole    2 moles

3 moles

Pressure is the result of gas molecules bombarding the walls of the vessel in which the gas is contained. Obviously the greater the number of molecules in a given volume, the greater the pressure will be. If the pressure of the sulphur dioxide/sulphur trioxide system increases, by Le Chatelier's principle, the equilibrium will shift to try to reduce this pressure. A reduction in pressure can be achieved by reducing the number of molecules, in other words by shifting the equilibrium to the right. In this way more sulphur dioxide is converted into sulphur trioxide. We would expect increased pressure to favour the formation of sulphur trioxide, and decreased pressure to favour the formation of sulphur dioxide.

**Effect of temperature**

$$2SO_2(g) + O_2(g) \rightleftharpoons 2SO_3(g) \qquad \Delta H = -385 \text{ kJ}$$

The sulphur dioxide/sulphur trioxide system is one which gives out heat in the conversion of sulphur dioxide to sulphur trioxide. If the temperature of this system is increased, then by Le Chatelier's principle, the equilibrium will shift to try to reduce this temperature. A reduction in temperature can be achieved by converting sulphur trioxide into sulphur dioxide, as this reaction requires heat. We would expect high temperatures to favour the formation of sulphur dioxide and low temperatures to favour the formation of sulphur trioxide.

By Le Chatelier's principle we would expect the contact process to use high pressures which favour the conversion of sulphur dioxide to sulphur trioxide. In fact a 98 per cent yield of sulphur trioxide is obtained at atmospheric pressure, so it is not economically necessary to raise the pressure.

Also by Le Chatelier's principle we would expect the contact process to use low temperatures which favour the production of sulphur trioxide. In fact at low temperatures the reaction rate becomes very slow, and from the information shown in Table 7.3 we can see that the most economic temperature lies somewhere between 673 K (400 °C) and 773 K (500 °C). The heat evolved in the reaction between sulphur dioxide and oxygen is used to preheat the entering reactants.

**Table 7.3** Percentage conversion to $SO_3$ at various temperatures

| Temperature of catalyst | | Percentage of $SO_3$ obtained |
|---|---|---|
| K | °C | |
| 673 | 400 | 86 |
| 707 | 434 | 99 |
| 823 | 550 | 85 |
| 913 | 640 | 60 |

We might expect the final step in the manufacture of sulphuric acid to be the dissolving of the sulphur trioxide in water according to the equation

$$SO_3(g) + H_2O(l) \rightarrow H_2SO_4(l)$$

In fact sulphur trioxide does not dissolve well in water, but forms a thick mist of sulphuric acid. The formation of such a mist would obviously be a great health hazard to those working in the sulphuric acid plant and would also seriously pollute the environment around the sulphuric acid plant. These dangers are overcome by taking up the sulphur trioxide gas in 97 per cent sulphuric acid. This results in the formation of oleum or fuming sulphuric acid, which can be diluted to give sulphuric acid of the required concentration.

$$SO_3(g) + H_2SO_4(l) \rightarrow H_2S_2O_7(l)$$

$$H_2S_2O_7(l) + H_2O(l) \rightarrow 2H_2SO_4(l)$$

The contact process produces sulphuric acid of an extremely high quality.

**(b) Haber Process**   The most important source of ammonia is the direct combination of nitrogen and hydrogen in the presence of a catalyst. Industrially this is done by the **Haber Process** (Figure 7.9). Nitrogen gas is obtained by the fractional distillation of liquid air. Hydrogen is obtained from natural gas ($CH_4$) by a process called steam reforming. The catalyst used in the Haber Process consists of small pieces of iron.

**Figure 7.9** The Haber Process

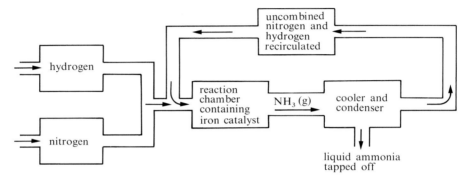

As shown by the equation, the reaction between nitrogen and hydrogen is reversible. In fact, under normal conditions, the equilibrium lies very much to the left, which means that the yield of ammonia is very small. The yield can, of course, be improved by changing the conditions. Let us apply Le Chatelier's principle.

**Effect of pressure**   $\underbrace{N_2(g) + 3H_2(g)}_{\text{4 moles}} \rightleftharpoons \underbrace{2NH_3(g)}_{\text{2 moles}}$

An increase in pressure will tend to make the equilibrium move in the direction which causes a decrease in pressure, that is from left to right. This means that nitrogen and hydrogen will combine to form ammonia. The Haber process uses high pressures of up to 200 times atmospheric pressure to increase the yield of ammonia.

**Effect of temperature**   $N_2(g) + 3H_2(g) \rightleftharpoons 2NH_3(g) \qquad \Delta H = -91 \text{ kJ}$

The reaction between nitrogen and hydrogen is exothermic. A decrease in temperature will tend to make the equilibrium move in the direction which causes an increase in temperature, that is from left to right. This favours the formation of ammonia.

In practice, low temperatures slow up the rate of the reaction too much, so the Haber process uses temperatures in the region of 770 K (500 °C) to 870 K (600 °C). Temperatures of this order result in a 40 per cent yield of ammonia. However, any unreacted gases can be recirculated into the reaction chamber, so that there is no wastage of the reactants.

In the Haber process, the ammonia is continually removed as it is formed by liquefying it. The reasons for this are twofold. Firstly, removal of the ammonia will stop it from decomposing. Secondly, constant removal of the ammonia means that more ammonia is always being formed in an attempt to establish equilibrium.

### Summary

From this chapter you should know:

1  Different reactions proceed at different rates.

2  Collision between particles is necessary for chemical reaction.

3  Molecules must possess a certain minimum energy before collisions will be effective.

4  How activated complexes form.

5  How the collision geometry will affect a reaction.

6  How to interpret potential energy diagrams.

7  How a catalyst affects the activation energy and hence the rate of reaction.

8  Which factors can affect the rate of reaction.

9  The meaning of equilibrium in chemical reactions.

10  How the effect of concentration, temperature, and pressure on equilibrium reactions can be explained in terms of Le Chatelier's principle.

### Questions

1    1

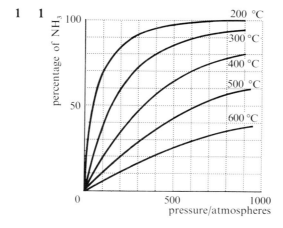

The graphs show the percentage of ammonia in the equilibrium mixture obtained by reacting a 1:3 mixture by volume of nitrogen and hydrogen at different temperatures and pressures.

   **1.1**   At what temperature and pressure does the equilibrium mixture contain the highest percentage of ammonia?

**1.2** State whether the formation of ammonia from its elements is an exothermic or an endothermic process, and explain how this can be deduced from the graphs.

**1.3** What yield of ammonia is obtained at 500 °C and 350 atmospheres pressure?

**1.4** Considering your answers to **1.1** and **1.3** above, explain why many industrial plants using this reaction are operated at 500 °C and 350 atmospheres pressure.

2 In the industrial process for the manufacture of ammonia explain:

**2.1** How the ammonia can be separated from the mixture of gases obtained.

**2.2** Why the gases are carefully purified before being passed into the reaction chamber.

**2.3** What is done to avoid waste of unreacted nitrogen and hydrogen.

3 Much of the ammonia manufactured is used to make ammonium sulphate for use as a fertiliser.

**3.1** Write the equation for the reaction employed to make this compound from ammonia.

**3.2** What effect will the addition of ammonium sulphate have on the pH of the soil? Explain your answer.

**3.3** How could you distinguish chemically between ammonium sulphate and another common fertiliser, ammonium nitrate? *SCEEB*

2 Ammonium nitrite decomposes thus when heated:

$$NH_4NO_2 \rightarrow 2H_2O + N_2$$

The rates of decomposition of 100 cm³ samples of each solution were followed under three different sets of conditions.

| | Concentration of solution (%) | Temperature of solution (°C) |
|---|---|---|
| Graph 1 | 5.0 | 80 |
| Graph 2 | 5.0 | 90 |
| Graph 3 | 2.5 | 80 |

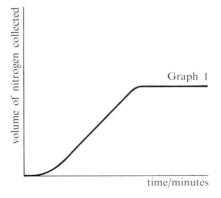

Draw one sketch showing all three graphs, labelling each clearly. Pay particular attention to the final volumes of nitrogen, and the slopes of the graphs. (no graph paper required). *SCEEB*

**3**

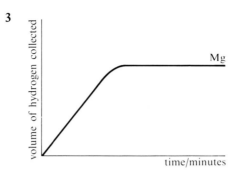

The graph shows how the volume of hydrogen released increases with time as 1 mole of magnesium reacts with excess dilute hydrochloric acid.
Copy the graph (no graph paper required) and add corresponding graphs for 1 mole of zinc and for 1 mole of sodium reacting. Label each clearly. Assume that the three metals have similar sizes of granules. *SCEEB*

**4**   Write an essay on 'Factors affecting the rate of chemical reactions'. In your answer you should refer to the following topics:

The range of reaction rates—from slow to very fast.
Effect on reaction rate of varying concentration, particle size, and temperature.
How the results can be explained by a collision theory and the idea of activation energy.
What a catalyst is and how it is thought to operate.
The meaning of the terms 'the mechanism of a reaction' and 'the rate-determining step'.

Your answer should be illustrated by examples. *SCEEB*

**5**   Write an essay on 'Catalysis'.
Your answer should refer to the following topics:

What a catalyst is and how it is thought to operate.
The effect of a catalyst on a system in equilibrium.
Some examples of the use of catalysts in the school laboratory.
Some examples of the use of catalysts in industrial processes, with comment on their economic importance. *SCEEB*

**6**   The following graph represents the energy changes involved in the reaction:

$$X_2 + Y_2 \rightleftharpoons 2XY$$

One line represents the catalysed reaction and the other the uncatalysed reaction.

In terms of the letters A, B, C, and D give:
1   The enthalpy change ($\Delta H$) for the forward reaction.
2   The activation energy for the catalysed forward reaction.
3   The activation energy for the uncatalysed reverse reaction. *P & W*

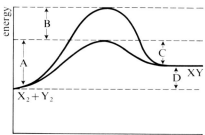

7   Discuss, with reference to a suitable example, the influence of concentration and catalysts on the position of equilibrium in a reversible reaction. Explain the following:

1   The pH of an aqueous solution of ethanoic acid rises when solid sodium ethanoate is added.

2   $SO_2(g) + \frac{1}{2}O_2(g) \rightleftharpoons SO_2(g)$      $\Delta H = -98 \text{ kJ mol}^{-1}$

A relatively low temperature (450 °C) is chosen as the operating temperature for the contact process.

3   A mixture of flour or coal dust in air is liable to explode. *P & W*

8       **1.1**   Draw a potential energy diagram for the system

$PCl_5 \rightleftharpoons PCl_3 + Cl_2$      $\Delta H = -126 \times 10^3 \text{ J mol}^{-1}$

Clearly mark the reactants, products and the position of the activated complex on your diagram.

**1.2**   Assuming that the potential energies of the reactants, products, and activated complex of a reaction are $70 \times 10^3$, $30 \times 10^3$, and $120 \times 10^3$ J mol$^{-1}$ respectively, calculate the activation energy and $\Delta H$ for the reaction.

2   Draw the potential energy curves for an uncatalysed and a catalysed reaction to show that you clearly understand the function of a catalyst.

3   Consider the following system at equilibrium

$\underset{\text{orange}}{Cr_2O_7^{2-}} + OH^- \rightleftharpoons \underset{\text{yellow}}{2CrO_4^{2-}} + H^+$

Explain how the position of equilibrium for the system could be changed and how you would recognize such changes.

4   Explain the effect of pressure and temperature changes on the reaction.

$A_2(g) + 2B_2(g) \rightleftharpoons 2AB_2(g)$      $\Delta H$ is positive      *P & W*

# 8 Hydrocarbons

## 8.1 The variety of organic compounds

The study of the vast field of organic chemistry is simplified by the existence of families of similar compounds called **homologous series**. Members of such series can be represented by a general formula and are characterized by similar methods of preparation and similar chemical properties. They also exhibit a regular gradation in physical properties such as melting points. The gradation is due to a regular increase in molecular size which causes an increase in the inter-molecular attractions (or Van der Waals' forces), and thus more energy is required to overcome these attractions.

## 8.2 The alkanes

Table 8.1 gives some information about the alkanes.

**Table 8.1** The alkanes

| Name | Molecular formula | Boiling point | | State at 293 K (20 °C) |
|---|---|---|---|---|
| | | K | °C | |
| methane | $CH_4$ | 109 | −164 | gas |
| ethane | $C_2H_6$ | 186 | −87 | gas |
| propane | $C_3H_8$ | 231 | −42 | gas |
| butane | $C_4H_{10}$ | 272.5 | −0.5 | gas |
| pentane | $C_5H_{12}$ | 309 | 36 | liquid |
| hexane | $C_6H_{14}$ | 342 | 69 | liquid |
| heptane | $C_7H_{16}$ | 371 | 98 | liquid |
| octane | $C_8H_{18}$ | 399 | 126 | liquid |
| nonane | $C_9H_{20}$ | 424 | 151 | liquid |
| decane | $C_{10}H_{22}$ | 447 | 174 | liquid |
| eicosane | $C_{20}H_{42}$ | 616 | 343 | solid |

**General formula**     The general formula of the alkane series is $C_nH_{2n+2}$.

**Method of preparation**     Commercially the alkanes are obtained by fractional distillation of crude oil, although the first member of the series, methane, often occurs naturally on its own. The alkanes can be prepared in the laboratory by decarboxylation (the removal of carbon dioxide) of the appropriate alkanoic acid. For example, methane is prepared by heating soda lime (calcium oxide slaked with sodium hydroxide) with ethanoic acid as shown in Figure 8.1.

**Figure 8.2** Laboratory preparation of ethene

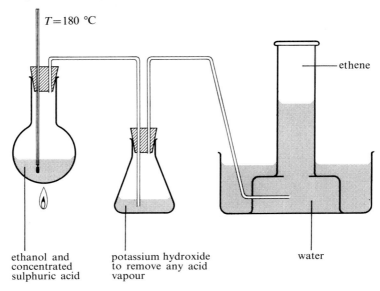

$T = 180\ ^\circ C$

ethene

ethanol and
concentrated
sulphuric acid

potassium hydroxide
to remove any acid
vapour

water

Alternatively, the dehydration process can be carried out by passing alcohol vapour over heated aluminium oxide (Figure 8.3).

**Figure 8.3** Preparation of ethene using aluminium oxide as the dehydrating agent.

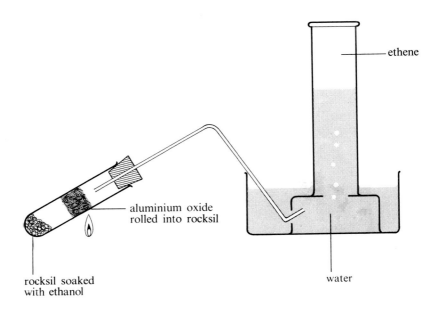

ethene

aluminium oxide
rolled into rocksil

rocksil soaked
with ethanol

water

## 8.4 Properties of alkenes

**Boiling point**   Table 8.2 illustrates the gradation in boiling point of the alkenes.

**Solubility**   Like the alkanes, the alkenes are insoluble in water, but soluble in tetrachloromethane.

**Combustion**   The alkenes burn to give carbon dioxide and water:

$$C_2H_4(g) + 3O_2(g) \rightarrow 2CO_2(g) + 2H_2O(g) \qquad \Delta H = -1410 \text{ kJ mol}^{-1}$$

Because of the higher proportion of carbon in the alkenes, they burn with a sootier flame than the alkanes.

**Reactivity**   The alkenes are generally a lot more reactive than the alkanes. This can be accounted for by their **unsaturated** nature, that is the existence of double bonds in their structure.

**Addition**   Due to their unsaturated nature, the alkenes react by addition, which means another species is simply added on as shown in the following examples.

1   With hydrogen

$$\begin{array}{c} CH_2 \\ \parallel \\ CH_2 \end{array} + H_2 \xrightarrow[140\,°C]{Ni\ catalyst} \begin{array}{c} CH_3 \\ | \\ CH_3 \end{array}$$

This process is known as **hydrogenation** and one example of its industrial use is the conversion of unsaturated vegetable oils to saturated fats in the manufacture of margarine.

2   With halogens

$$\begin{array}{c} CH_2 \\ \parallel \\ CH_2 \end{array} + Cl_2 \rightarrow \begin{array}{c} CH_2.Cl \\ | \\ CH_2.Cl \end{array}$$
1,2-dichloroethane

3   With halogen acids

$$\begin{array}{c} CH_2 \\ \parallel \\ CH_2 \end{array} + HI \rightarrow \begin{array}{c} CH_3 \\ | \\ CH_2.I \end{array}$$
iodoethane

4   With concentrated sulphuric acid

$$\begin{array}{c} CH_2 \\ \parallel \\ CH_2 \end{array} + H_2SO_4 \rightarrow \begin{array}{c} CH_3 \\ | \\ CH_2.O.SO_2.OH \end{array}$$
ethyl hydrogensulphate

Since this reaction is not shared by the alkanes, it is useful in the laboratory for separating mixtures of alkanes and alkenes. In the refining of oil, concentrated sulphuric acid is used to remove unsaturated alkenes from petrol, which would otherwise react to form gums. The sulphuric acid also removes certain unwanted sulphur compounds.

5   With bromine water

Ethene decolorizes bromine water with the formation of 1,2-dibromoethane.

$$\begin{array}{l} CH_2 \\ \| \\ CH_2 \end{array} + Br_2 \rightarrow \begin{array}{l} CH_2.Br \\ | \\ CH_2.Br \end{array}$$
$$\text{1,2-dibromoethane}$$

This reaction is used as a test for the presence of an unsaturated hydrocarbon.

6   With neutral, or slightly alkaline potassium manganate(VII) solution.

$$\begin{array}{l} CH_2 \\ \| \\ CH_2 \end{array} + 2KMnO_4 + 4H_2O \rightarrow 2KOH + 2MnO_2 + \begin{array}{l} CH_2.OH \\ | \\ CH_2.OH \end{array}$$
$$\text{ethane-1,2-diol}$$

The product ethane-1,2-diol is more commonly known as ethylene glycol and it is sold as antifreeze.

**Polymerization**   At high temperatures and pressures, or in the presence of a catalyst, the alkenes will link together to form polymers.

Poly(ethene)   Due to their unsaturated nature, alkenes will add to each other, or **polymerize**:

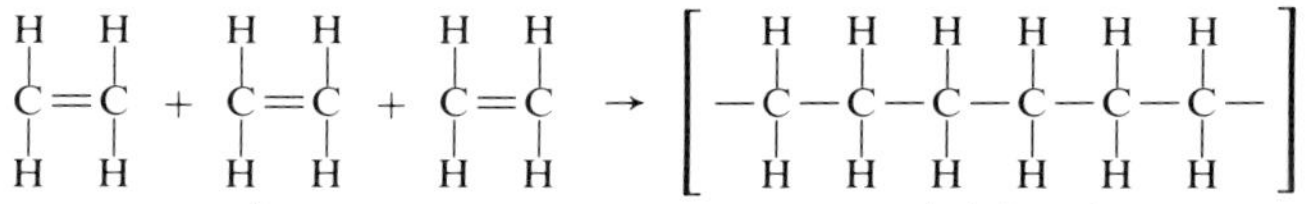

ethene
monomers

poly(ethene)
polymer

This is a reaction of great industrial importance, as it is the whole foundation of the plastics industry.

Uses: detergent bottles; washing-up bowls; water-storage tanks; aircraft construction kits; artificial ski slopes.

Poly(chloroethene)   PVC (polyvinyl chloride) is an addition polymer and is obtained by polymerizing chloroethene (vinyl chloride).

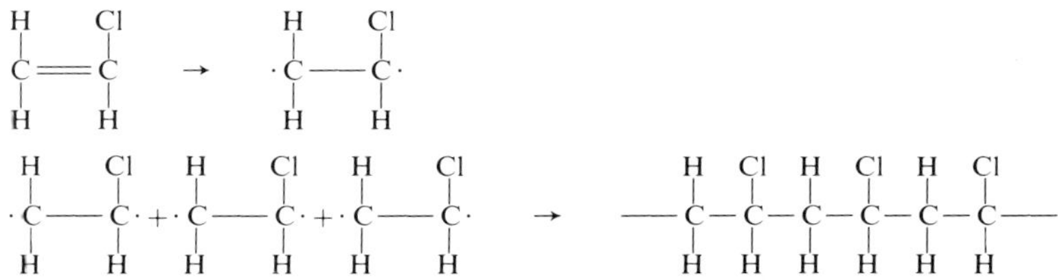

poly(chloroethene) or polyvinyl chloride

Uses: gramophone records; electric cable coverings; hose pipes; baby pants; floor tiles; wall-paper; curtain rails; raincoats; roofing; handle-bar grips; guttering; film; insulators; shoes; coated fabrics.

PTFE   Poly(tetrafluoroethene) is an addition polymer obtained by polymerizing tetrafluoroethene. The mechanism is similar to that in the formation of PVC.

$$-\!\!-\overset{\displaystyle F}{\underset{\displaystyle F}{C}}-\overset{\displaystyle F}{\underset{\displaystyle F}{C}}-\overset{\displaystyle F}{\underset{\displaystyle F}{C}}-\overset{\displaystyle F}{\underset{\displaystyle F}{C}}-\overset{\displaystyle F}{\underset{\displaystyle F}{C}}-\overset{\displaystyle F}{\underset{\displaystyle F}{C}}-\!\!-$$

poly(tetrafluoroethene)   (PTFE)

Uses: the Teflon 'non-stick' in frying pans.

Perspex   Perspex is poly(methyl 2- methylpropenoate). It is obtained in a similar way to PVC by polymerizing methyl 2-methylpropenoate (methyl methacrylate).

$$-\!\!-\overset{\displaystyle H}{\underset{\displaystyle H}{C}}-\overset{\displaystyle CH_3}{\underset{\displaystyle CO_2CH_3}{C}}-\!\!\!\!-\overset{\displaystyle H}{\underset{\displaystyle H}{C}}-\overset{\displaystyle CH_3}{\underset{\displaystyle CO_2CH_3}{C}}-\!\!\!\!-\overset{\displaystyle H}{\underset{\displaystyle H}{C}}-\overset{\displaystyle CH_3}{\underset{\displaystyle CO_2CH_3}{C}}-\!\!-$$

poly(methyl 2-methylpropenoate)   (perspex)

Uses: telephone parts; windows in aircraft; dentures; artificial eyes; lighting fittings; glass-clear mouldings.

Polystyrene   Polystyrene is poly(phenylethene) and is obtained by the addition polymerization of phenylethene (styrene). The mechanism is similar to that in the formation of PVC.

$$\overset{\displaystyle H}{\underset{\displaystyle H}{C}}\!=\!\overset{\displaystyle C_6H_5}{\underset{\displaystyle H}{C}} + \overset{\displaystyle H}{\underset{\displaystyle H}{C}}\!=\!\overset{\displaystyle C_6H_5}{\underset{\displaystyle H}{C}} + \overset{\displaystyle H}{\underset{\displaystyle H}{C}}\!=\!\overset{\displaystyle C_6H_5}{\underset{\displaystyle H}{C}} \rightarrow -\overset{\displaystyle H}{\underset{\displaystyle H}{C}}-\overset{\displaystyle C_6H_5}{\underset{\displaystyle H}{C}}-\overset{\displaystyle H}{\underset{\displaystyle H}{C}}-\overset{\displaystyle C_6H_5}{\underset{\displaystyle H}{C}}-\overset{\displaystyle H}{\underset{\displaystyle H}{C}}-\overset{\displaystyle C_6H_5}{\underset{\displaystyle H}{C}}-$$

poly(phenylethene)   polystyrene

Uses: food containers and packaging; cosmetic bottles; television cabinets; 'plastic' cups; ceiling tiles; apple trays.

## 8.5 Isomerism and nomenclature

Compounds with the same molecular formula but different structural formulae are called **isomers**. All but the first three alkanes and the first two alkenes exhibit isomerism within their respective homologous series. The structural formulae shown are diagrammatic representations of the actual structures. You should remember that the covalent bonds around a carbon atom are not planar, but are directed to the four corners of a tetrahedron. Consider the following examples.

The alkenes have more isomers than the corresponding alkanes, because the structural formulae can differ due to the position of the branching chains and also the position of the double bond.

To enable us to distinguish between isomers, organic compounds are named systematically.

| Alkane | Structural formula | Alkene | Structural formula |
|---|---|---|---|
| butane $C_4H_{10}$ | | butene $C_4H_8$ | |
| pentane $C_5H_{12}$ | | pentene $C_5H_{10}$ | |

Hexane, $C_6H_{14}$, has five isomers.
Hexene, $C_6H_{12}$, has nine isomers.

**Naming the alkanes**   The rules for naming the alkanes are very simple.

1   Take the longest unbranched carbon chain as the parent:

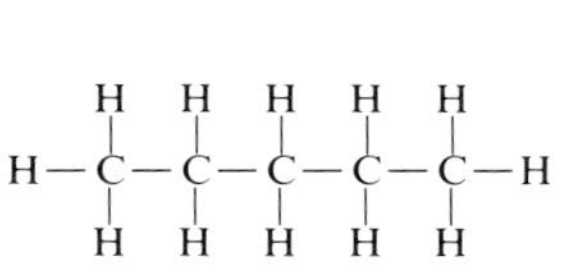

pentane 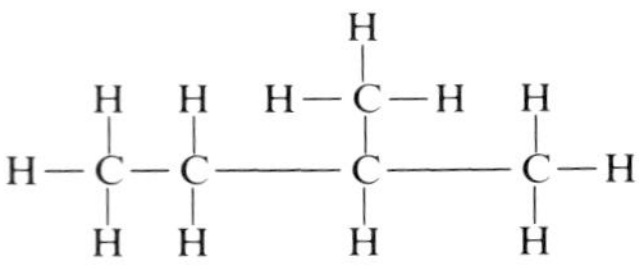   butane 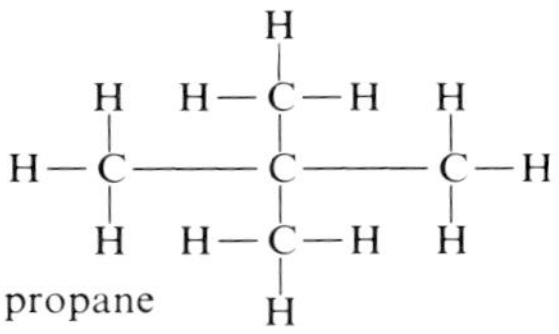   propane

2   Name the branches:

—CH$_3$   methyl
—C$_2$H$_5$   ethyl
—C$_3$H$_7$   propyl

3   Indicate the number of branches:

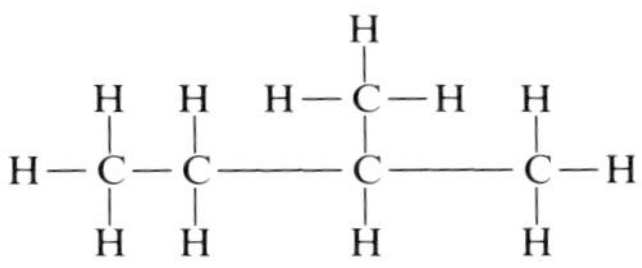

methylbutane 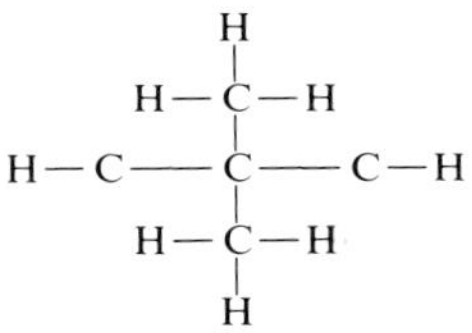   dimethylpropane

4   Indicate the position of the branches by a number (always numbering the parent chain from the end nearest the branches):

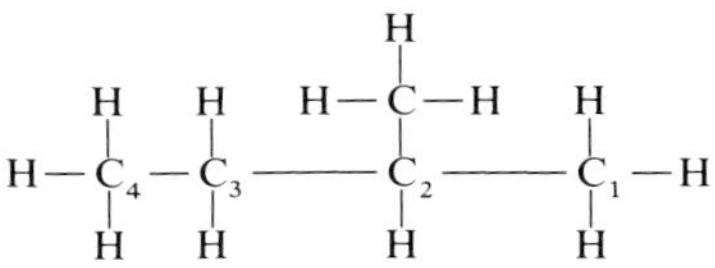

2-methylbutane 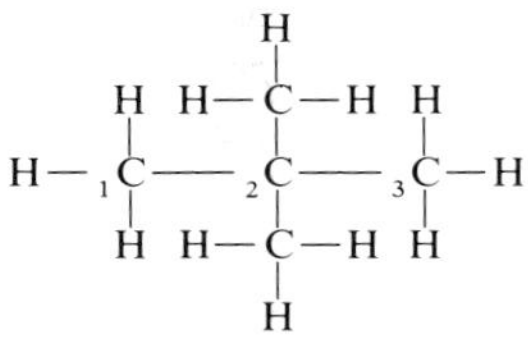   2,2-dimethylpropane

Some further examples of the systematic naming of alkanes are shown below:

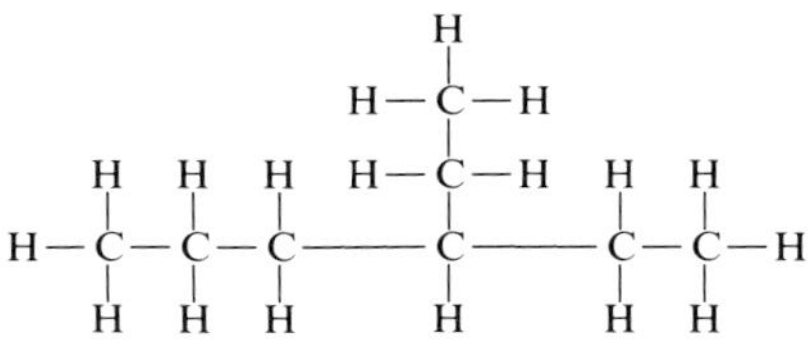

3-ethylhexane 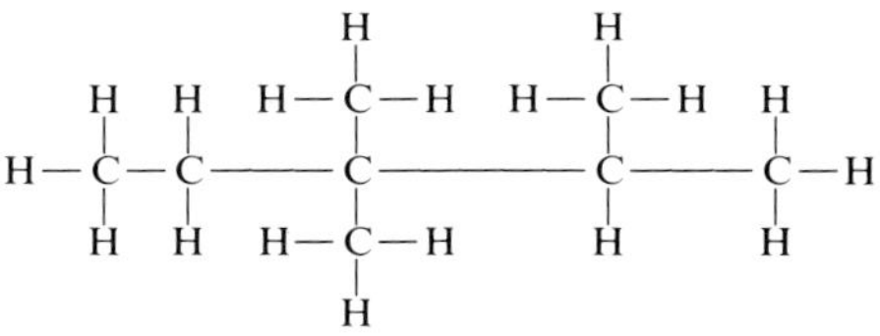   2,3,3-trimethylpentane

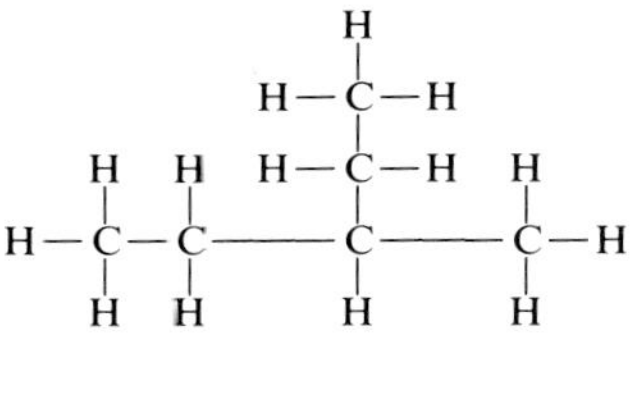

3-methylpentane

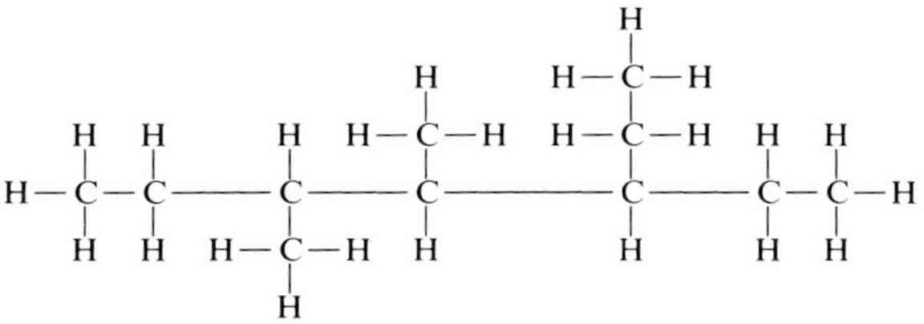

3-ethyl-4, 5-dimethylheptane

**Naming the alkenes**    The rules for naming the alkenes are similar to those for the alkanes.

1    Take the longest unbranched carbon chain containing the double bond as the parent:

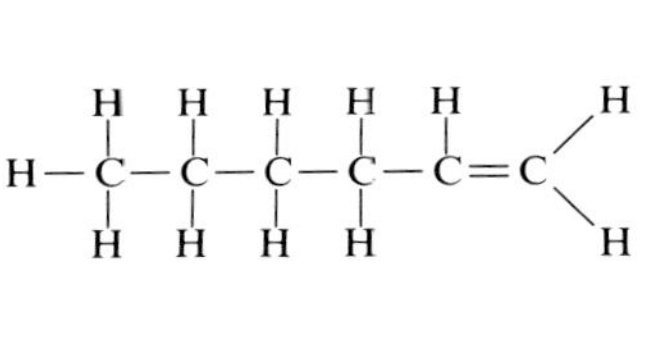

hexene

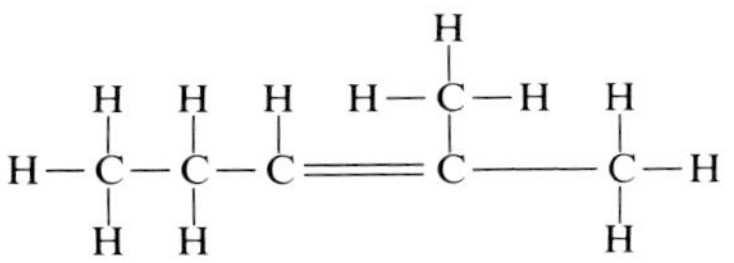

pentene

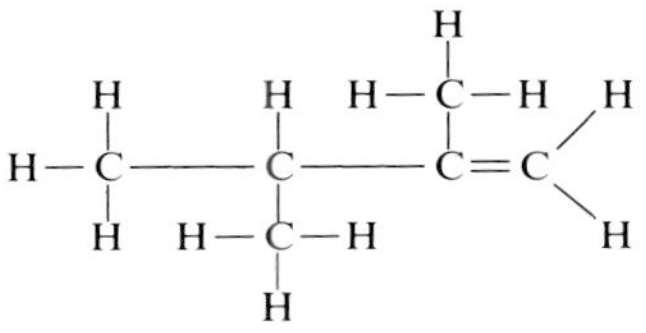

butene

2    Number the carbon atoms from the end nearest the double bond:

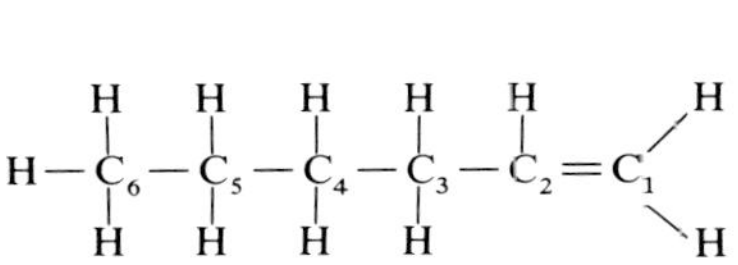

hex-1-ene

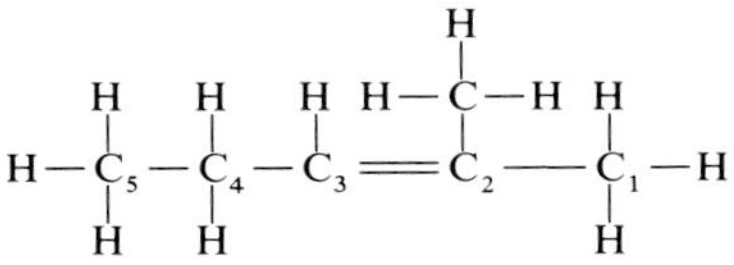

pent-2-ene

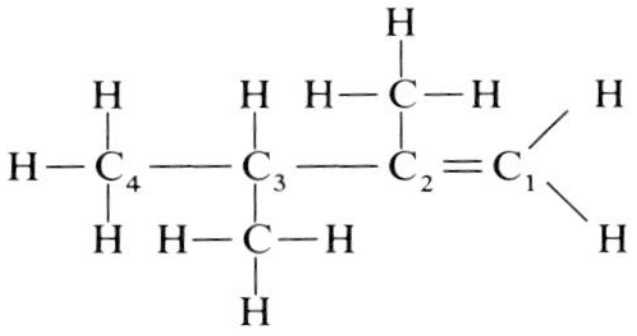

but-1-ene

*Note* The name hex-1-ene indicates that the double bond lies between carbon atoms one and two, the name pent-2-ene indicates that the double bond lies between carbon atoms two and three.

3    Name the branches:

—CH$_3$    methyl
—C$_2$H$_5$    ethyl
—C$_3$H$_7$    propyl

4    Indicate the number of branches:

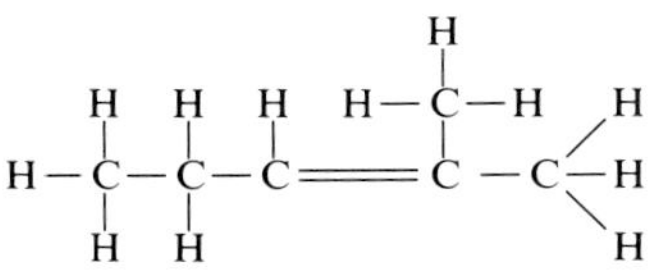

methylpent-2-ene

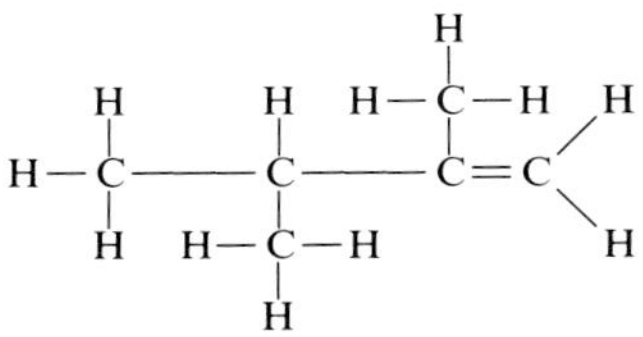

dimethylbut-1-ene

**5** Indicate the position of the branches by a number (always numbering the parent chain from the end nearest the double bond):

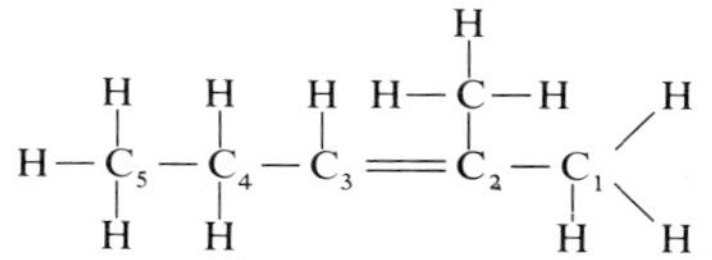

2-methylpent-2-ene 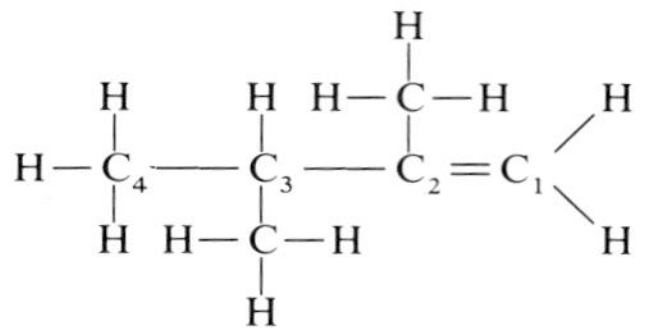                2,3-dimethylbut-1-ene

## 8.6 The alkynes

Ethyne (acetylene), $C_2H_2$, is the first member of the alkyne series, a series in which two of the carbon atoms are joined together by a triple covalent bond.

Table 8.3 gives some information about the alkynes.

**Table 8.3** The alkynes

| Name | Molecular formula | Boiling point | | State at 293 K (20 °C) |
|------|------|------|------|------|
| | | K | °C | |
| ethyne | $C_2H_2$ | 189 | −84 | gas |
| propyne | $C_3H_4$ | 250 | −23 | gas |
| butyne | $C_4H_6$ | 281 | 8 | gas |
| pentyne | $C_5H_8$ | 313 | 40 | liquid |

**General formula**  We can see from Table 8.3 that the general formula for the alkyne series is $C_nH_{2n-2}$ and that they exhibit a gradation in boiling point in the same way as other homologous series.

**Method of preparation**  **1** In the laboratory alkynes can be prepared by the action of alcoholic potassium hydroxide on dibromoalkanes, which have the bromine atoms on adjacent carbon atoms.

$$\begin{array}{c} CH_2.Br \\ | \\ CH_2.Br \end{array} \xrightarrow{\ KOH/C_2H_5OH\ } \begin{array}{c} CH \\ ||| \\ CH \end{array} + 2HBr$$

ethyne

**2** However, ethyne can be prepared conveniently by the action of water on calcium carbide.

$$CaC_2 + 2H_2O \rightarrow \begin{array}{c} CH \\ ||| \\ CH \end{array} + Ca(OH)_2$$

It should be noted that this is not a general method of preparation of alkynes.

### 8.7  Properties of alkynes

**Solubility**    Ethyne is insoluble in water, but soluble in non-polar solvents.

**Combustion**    Ethyne burns in a good supply of oxygen to form carbon dioxide and water.

$$2C_2H_2(g) + 5O_2(g) \rightarrow 4CO_2(g) + 2H_2O(g)$$

If it is used in a special burner with an extra oxygen supply, ethyne burns brilliantly giving the very hot oxy-acetylene flame which is capable of cutting through metals.

When a sample of ethyne is tested with a lighted taper it burns with a yellow, sooty flame according to the following equation:

$$2C_2H_2(g) + O_2(g) \rightarrow 4C(s) + 2H_2O(g)$$

**Addition**    Alkynes undergo addition reactions as shown in the following examples:

1    With hydrogen

The reaction proceeds in two stages, an alkene being formed as an intermediate.

$$\begin{array}{ccc} CH & CH_2 & CH_3 \\ ||| & || & | \\ CH & CH_2 & CH_3 \\ \text{ethyne} & \text{ethene} & \text{ethane} \end{array}$$
$\xrightarrow[\text{catalyst}]{H_2}$   $\xrightarrow[\text{catalyst}]{H_2}$

2    With halogens

Chlorine reacts explosively with ethyne producing carbon and hydrogen chloride gas.

$$C_2H_2(g) + Cl_2(g) \rightarrow 2C(s) + 2HCl(g)$$

With bromine water there is no immediate reaction as might have been expected. The bromine water does, however, decolorize slowly. Because of the slow decolorization of bromine water by alkynes, we can say that immediate decolorization of bromine water is a specific test for an alkene when testing hydrocarbons for unsaturation.

3    With halogen acids

Ethyne reacts with hydrogen chloride to form chloroethene (vinyl chloride), which is used in the production of poly(chloroethene) or P.V.C.

$$\begin{array}{ccccc} CH & & CHCl & & CHCl_2 \\ ||| & + HCl \rightarrow & || & + HCl \rightarrow & | \\ CH & & CH_2 & & CH_3 \\ \text{ethyne} & & \text{chloroethene} & & \text{1,1-dichloroethane} \end{array}$$

4    With water and dilute sulphuric acid/mercury(II) sulphate as catalyst, the alkyne is oxidized to the corresponding aldehyde, ethanal.

$$\begin{array}{ccc} CH & & CH_3 \\ ||| & + H_2O \xrightarrow[HgSO_4]{H_2SO_4(aq)} & | \\ CH & & CHO \\ \text{ethyne} & & \text{ethanal} \end{array}$$

**Substitution**　When ethyne is bubbled through ammoniacal solutions of copper(I) chloride or silver (I) nitrate, metal derivatives called acetylides are formed.

$$\begin{array}{c} CH \\ ||| \\ CH \end{array} + Cu_2Cl_2/NH_3 \rightarrow \begin{array}{c} C.Cu \\ ||| \\ C.Cu \end{array}$$

ethyne　　　　　　　　　　copper acetylide (red precipitate)

$$\begin{array}{c} CH \\ ||| \\ CH \end{array} + AgNO_3/NH_3 \rightarrow \begin{array}{c} C.Ag \\ ||| \\ C.Ag \end{array}$$

　　　　　　　　　　silver acetylide (yellow precipitate)

Both of these compounds are unstable and decompose explosively when dry.

## 8.8  Bonding in hydrocarbons

**Bond energy**　If we consider the structural formulae for ethane, ethene and ethyne, we might expect that the bond dissociation energy of the C=C bond would be twice the C—C bond value, and that the C≡C bond energy would be three times that of the C—C bond energy.

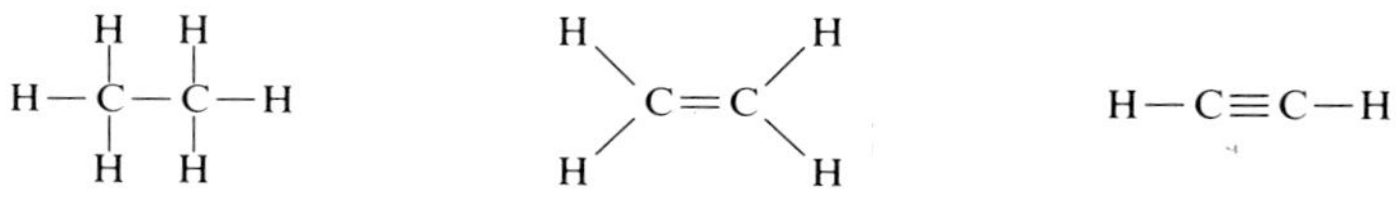

$$H-\overset{\overset{\displaystyle H}{|}}{\underset{\underset{\displaystyle H}{|}}{C}}-\overset{\overset{\displaystyle H}{|}}{\underset{\underset{\displaystyle H}{|}}{C}}-H \qquad \overset{H}{\underset{H}{>}}C=C\overset{H}{\underset{H}{<}} \qquad H-C\equiv C-H$$

However, when we look at the values in Table 8.4 we see that this is not so.

**Table 8.4**

| Bond | Bond disociation energy kJ mol$^{-1}$ |
|------|------|
| C—C | 347 |
| C=C | 608 |
| C≡C | 830 |

We shall have to look at the bonding system in more detail to explain this.

**Structure of molecules**　In a molecule of methane the bond angles are 109° 28′ corresponding to the tetrahedral arrangement of hydrogen atoms about the carbon.

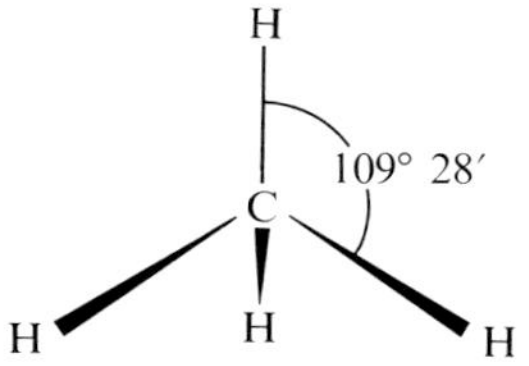

methane

Molecules of alkanes have the tetrahedral bond system extended.

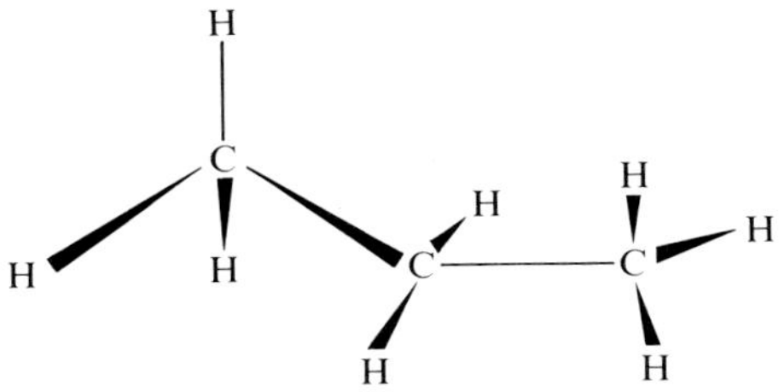

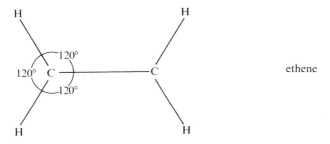

propane

However, the molecule of ethene $C_2H_4$ is planar and the bond angles are each 120°.

H $\qquad$ 120° $\qquad$ H

120° C $\longrightarrow$ C

120°

H $\qquad$ H

ethene

The molecule of ethyne $C_2H_2$ is linear, and the bond angles are 180°.

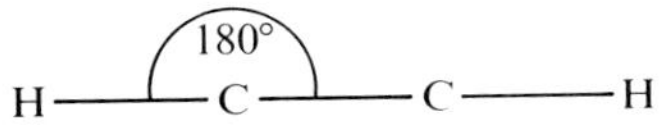

H $\longrightarrow$ C $\longrightarrow$ C $\longrightarrow$ H  180°

ethyne

**Bonding in molecules**

Up to this point all bonding has been explained in terms of overlapping electron clouds. This is called $\sigma$-bonding (sigma-bonding).

In the molecules of ethene and ethyne there are electrons not being used in the $\sigma$-bonding, one electron per carbon atom in the case of ethene and two electrons per carbon atom in the case of ethyne. These electrons become associated with both carbon atoms forming new electron clouds. This is called **$\pi$-bonding** (pi-bonding).

In ethene the new electron clouds are formed above and below the plane of the molecule.

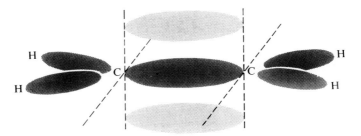

There are two intra-molecular bonds between the carbon atoms in ethene, one $\sigma$-bond and one $\pi$-bond, hence the bond energy value does not correspond to two $\sigma$-bonds.

In ethyne the new electron clouds are formed both above and below the molecule and on either side.

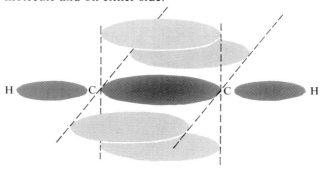

There are three intra-molecular bonds between the carbon atoms in ethyne one $\sigma$-bond, two $\pi$-bonds, hence the bond energy value does not correspond to three $\sigma$-bonds.

## 8.9 Cyclic compounds

Compounds in which the carbon atoms join up to form a ring are called cyclic compounds.

The cycloalkanes have similar properties to the alkanes.

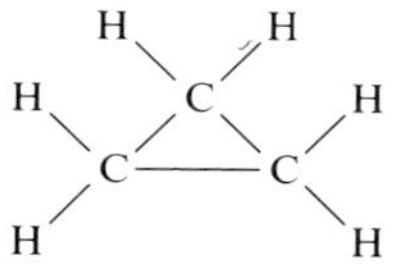

cyclopropane
$C_3H_6$

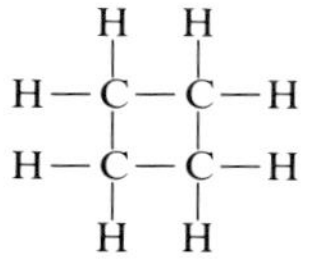

cyclobutane
$C_4H_8$

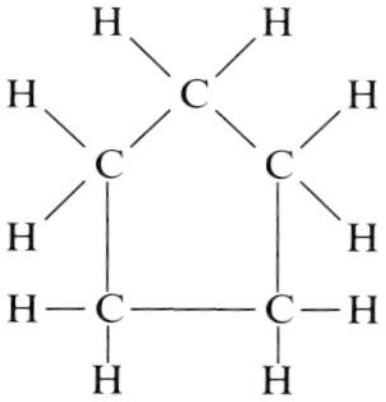

cyclopentane
$C_5H_{10}$

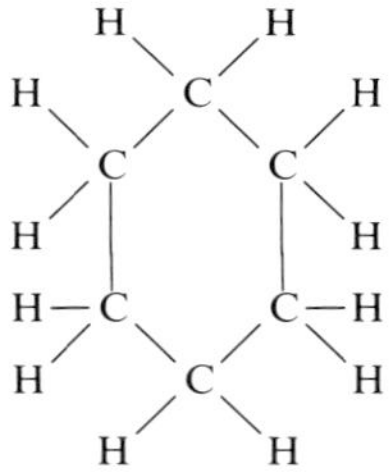

cyclohexane
$C_6H_{12}$

The cycloalkenes have similar properties to the alkenes.

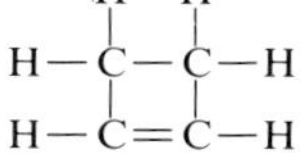

cyclobutene
$C_4H_6$

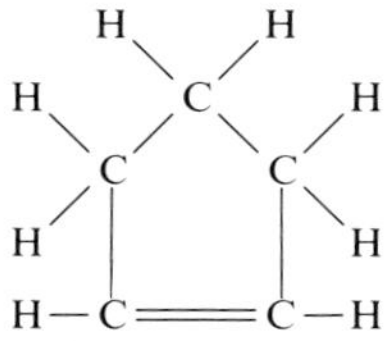

cyclopentene
$C_5H_8$

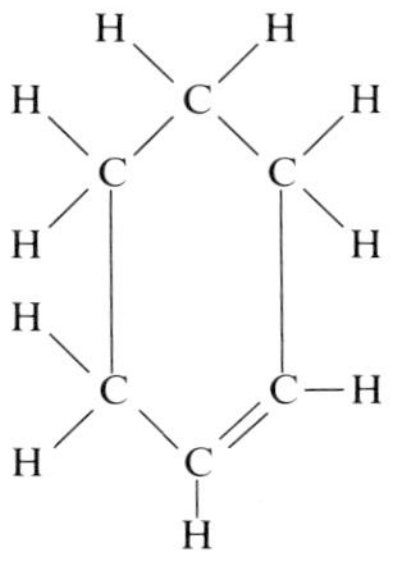

cyclohexene
$C_6H_{10}$

*Note* The general formula for the cycloalkanes corresponds to the general formula of the alkenes, i.e. the cycloalkanes and the alkenes are isomers. Similarly the cycloalkenes and the alkynes are isomers.

## 8.10  Aromatic compounds

The term 'aromatic' was originally applied to substances which had a sweet smell. It is now taken to mean the compound benzene, $C_6H_6$, or compounds which have similar structures and properties to benzene.

It would appear from the formula that benzene is a highly unsaturated compound;

possibly a chain compound
with triple bonds

$$H-C\equiv C-\underset{\underset{H}{|}}{\overset{\overset{H}{|}}{C}}-\underset{\underset{H}{|}}{\overset{\overset{H}{|}}{C}}-C\equiv C-H$$

or a ring compound
with double bonds.

Benzene does not decolorize bromine water as other unsaturated compounds do, so none of the structures suggested is satisfactory.

**Bonding**    X-ray analysis of benzene indicates

1    The bond angles are all 120°.
2    The molecule is a regular hexagon.
3    The C—C bond lengths are intermediate between C—C and C=C.

C—C bond length in methane  = 0.154 nm

C=C bond length in ethene    = 0.134 nm

C—C bond length in benzene  = 0.139 nm

As in the case of ethene there is one electron per carbon atom which is not being used, and these electrons become associated with all the carbon atoms forming new electron clouds.

These electrons are said to be delocalized.

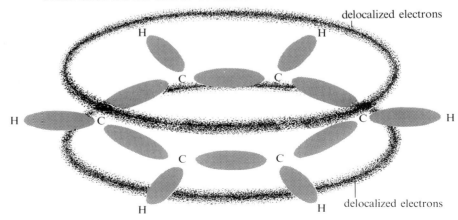

This is often simplified to

The structures of some other aromatic compounds are shown below.

toluene 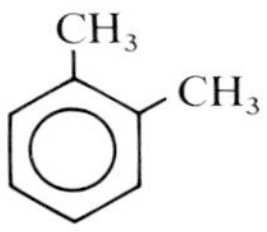                    xylene                    naphthalene                    anthracene

### 8.11 Benzene

**Method of preparation**   The principal sources of the aromatic hydrocarbons are coal tar and petroleum. Benzene can also be prepared by **dehydrogenation** of hexane.

$$C_6H_{14} \xrightarrow[\text{platinum catalyst}]{20 \text{ atmospheres } 500\,°C} C_6H_6 + 4H_2$$
hexane                    benzene

**Properties**   *Note* Benzene is a carcinogen and the following reactions can be carried out in the laboratory using toluene.

Solubility   Like the other hydrocarbons, benzene does not dissolve in water: as benzene is a liquid, we usually refer to it as being immiscible with water.

Combustion   Benzene burns to form carbon dioxide and water.

$$2C_6H_6(l) + 15O_2(g) \rightarrow 12CO_2(g) + 6H_2O(g)$$

Due to the high proportion of carbon in benzene the flame is very sooty when the oxygen supply is limited.

Substitution   Benzene undergoes substitution reactions in a similar fashion to the alkanes, although not so readily.

With bromine in the presence of an iron catalyst, bromobenzene is formed.

$$C_6H_6(l) + Br_2(l) \rightarrow C_6H_5Br(l) + HBr(g)$$
bromobenzene

Further substitution leads to the formation of hexabromobenzene $C_6Br_6$. An important step in the manufacture of certain explosives involves the nitration of aromatic compounds.

$$C_6H_6(l) + HNO_3(l) \xrightarrow{H_2SO_4} C_6H_5NO_2(l) + H_2O(l)$$
nitrobenzene

You will have heard of the explosive T.N.T. which is trinitrotoluene.

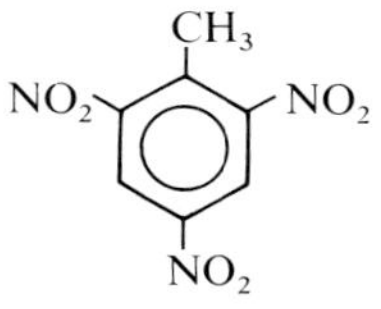

Addition Benzene does not undergo the simple addition of bromine water as do the unsaturated hydrocarbons, however, it is possible to add onto the benzene ring.

$$C_6H_6(l) + 3Br_2(l) \xrightarrow{\text{sunlight}} C_6H_6Br_6(l)$$
$$\text{hexabromocyclohexane}$$

### Summary

From this chapter you should know:

1 Members of a homologous series
    can be represented by a general formula
    can be prepared by similar methods
    exhibit a gradation in physical properties
    exhibit similar chemical properties

2 The alkanes are saturated and react by substitution.

3 The alkenes are unsaturated and react by addition.

4 The alkynes are unsaturated and react by substitution and addition.

5 That isomers of a compound have the same molecular but different structural formulae.

6 How to name an organic compound systematically.

7 The difference between $\sigma$ and $\pi$ bonding.

8 That benzene is an unsaturated compound but that it is not ethenic and its structure is explained by the presence of delocalized electrons.

9 The properties of benzene.

### Questions

See page 146

# 9 Functional groups

Investigation of the structural formulae of organic compounds shows the existence of a large number of similar groups which consist of carbon and hydrogen atoms only and have the general formula $C_nH_{2n+1}$. These are called the **alkyl groups**.

| | | | |
|---|---|---|---|
| $-CH_3$ | methyl | $-C_3H_7$ | propyl |
| $-C_2H_5$ | ethyl | $-C_4H_9$ | butyl |

If hydrogen atoms are attached to the alkyl groups then the resulting compounds are the alkanes.

| | | | |
|---|---|---|---|
| $CH_4$ | methane | $C_3H_8$ | propane |
| $C_2H_6$ | ethane | $C_4H_{10}$ | butane |

If other groups of atoms are attached to the alkyl group then different compounds are formed. There is a relatively small number of such groups and they impart characteristic properties to the molecule. Because of these properties the groups are called **functional groups**. Table 9.1 gives the names and structures of the most common functional groups and examples of the compounds formed.

**Table 9.1**

| Name of functional group | Structure | Compound |
|---|---|---|
| hydroxyl | $-OH$ | ethanol $C_2H_5OH$ |
| carbonyl (aldehyde) | 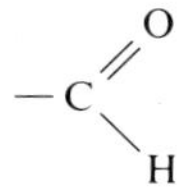 $-C{\overset{\displaystyle O}{\diagdown}}_H$ | ethanal $CH_3CHO$ |
| carbonyl (ketone) | 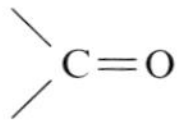 $>C=O$ | propanone $CH_3.CO.CH_3$ |
| carboxylic acid | 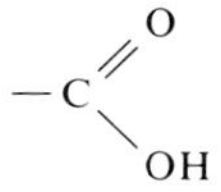 $-C{\overset{\displaystyle O}{\diagdown}}_{OH}$ | ethanoic acid $CH_3COOH$ |
| amino | $-NH_2$ | methylamine $CH_3NH_2$ |
| halide | $-Cl$ | chloroethane $C_2H_5Cl$ |

### 9.1 Alcohols

**Monohydric alcohols**   All alcohols have at least one hydroxyl group in the molecule. If they have only one such group they are known as monohydric alcohols. Table 9.2 gives some information about the monohydric alcohols.

**Table 9.2**

| | | Boiling point | |
|---|---|---|---|
| Formula | Name | K | °C |
| $CH_3OH$ | methanol | 337 | 64 |
| $C_2H_5OH$ | ethanol | 352 | 79 |
| $C_3H_7OH$ | propanol | 370 | 97 |
| $C_4H_9OH$ | butanol | 390 | 117 |

**Isomerism and nomenclature**   From the third member of the series onwards the alcohols exhibit isomerism within the series.

The isomers can differ in the placing of the branches:

methylpropanol   and   butanol

or in the placing of the hydroxyl group:

propan-1-ol   and   propan-2-ol

The rules for naming the alcohols are:

1   Take the longest carbon chain as the parent.

2   Number from the end nearest the hydroxyl group.

3   Indicate the position of the hydroxyl group.

4   Indicate the number and position of the branches in the same way as for the alkanes and alkenes.

Some examples are shown below:

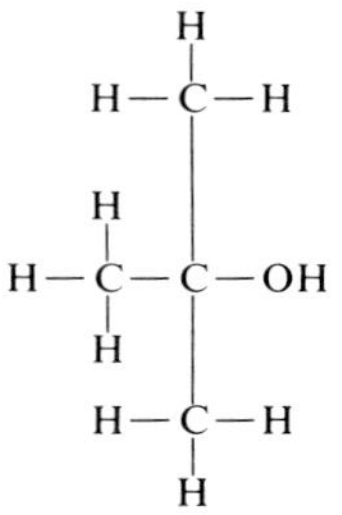

2-methylpropan-2-ol

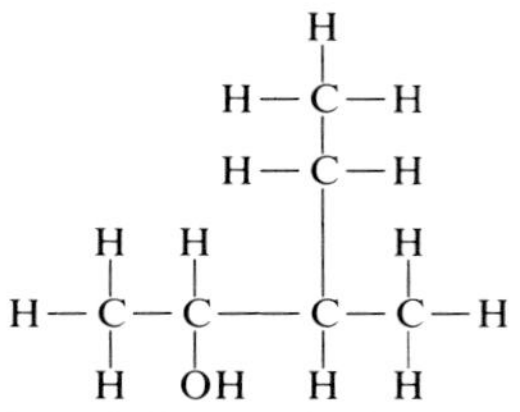

3-methylpentan-2-ol

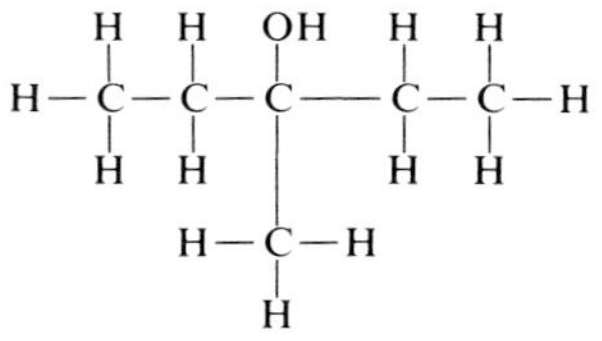

3-methylpentan-3-ol

**Preparing alcohols**  Ethanol can be obtained from the fermentation of starch, a process which involves the naturally occurring enzymes found in malt and yeast. The starch is first hydrolysed to maltose, a disaccharide, by the enzyme diastase found in malt.

$$2(C_6H_{10}O_5)_n + nH_2O \xrightarrow{\text{diastase}} nC_{12}H_{22}O_{11}$$
starch                                        maltose

The maltose is hydrolzed further to the monosaccharide glucose by the enzyme maltase, which is found in yeast.

$$C_{12}H_{22}O_{11} + H_2O \xrightarrow{\text{maltase}} 2C_6H_{12}O_6$$
maltose                                  glucose

Finally the glucose is converted into ethanol by the enzyme zymase, which is also found in yeast.

$$C_6H_{12}O_6 \xrightarrow{\text{zymase}} 2C_2H_5OH + 2CO_2$$
glucose                    ethanol

This process is utilized by brewers and distillers in the preparation of alcoholic drinks.

Ethanol for industrial use is produced by the petrochemical industry in the following manner. Ethene is treated with steam at a high temperature and pressure in the presence of a catalyst, and an addition reaction takes place.

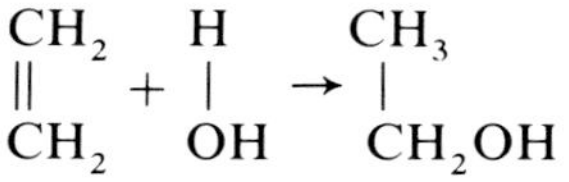

$$\begin{array}{ccc} CH_2 & H & CH_3 \\ \| & + \mid & \rightarrow \mid \\ CH_2 & OH & CH_2OH \end{array}$$

Other members of the alcohol series are also produced in this manner by hydrating the appropriate alkene.

In the laboratory, alcohols may be conveniently prepared by boiling the appropriate alkyl halide with sodium hydroxide solution.

RX + NaOH → ROH + NaX
alkyl halide          alcohol

Alkyl halides, as the name suggests, are alkyl groups attached to halogen atoms.

$C_2H_5Cl$   ethyl chloride or chloroethane

$C_4H_9Br$   butyl bromide or bromobutane

Alkyl halides are particularly suitable for this reaction because the bond between the halogen atom and the carbon atom is polar and hence readily susceptible to attack by an ionic substance like sodium hydroxide. The mechanism for the reaction is that shown below.

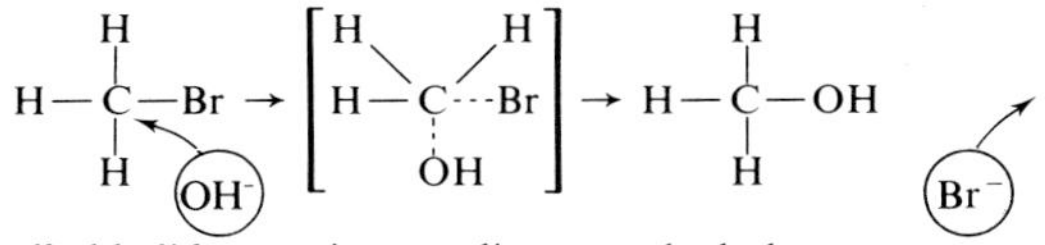

alkyl halide          intermediate          alcohol

## Properties of alcohols

Melting point and boiling point

As with other homologous series, the alcohols exhibit a gradation in melting point and boiling point, the lower members being volatile liquids and the higher members solids at room temperature. The alcohols do have higher melting points and boiling points than the corresponding alkanes. This is due to hydrogen bonding between alcohol molecules, which means that more energy has to be supplied to overcome these inter-molecular attractions.

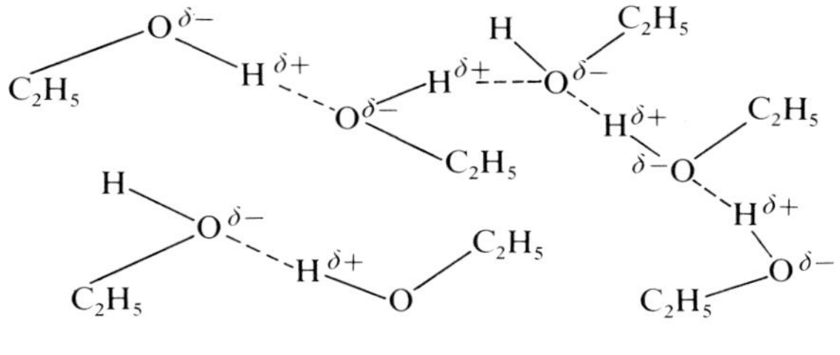

Solubility

The lower members of the alcohol series are miscible with water because of the polar nature of the hydroxyl group.

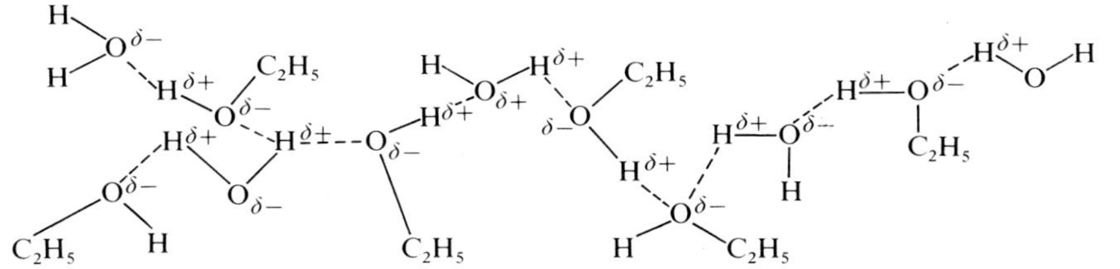

The higher members are insoluble. This is because the large hydrocarbon part of the alcohol molecule masks the smaller polar part.

Some of the most important industrial uses of alcohols are as solvents. Owing to their dual character, hydrophobic at one end and hydrophilic at the other end, alcohols dissolve both covalent and ionic substances.

**Comparison with water**   In the preceding examples, the alcohol molecule has been drawn as if it had a similar structure to the water molecule.

Alcohols do exhibit similar properties to water. The following examples illustrate the similarity.

**Reaction with sodium**   Hydrogen gas and sodium ethoxide are formed.

$$2C_2H_5OH + 2Na \rightarrow 2C_2H_5ONa + H_2$$
ethanol                    sodium ethoxide

Compare this reaction with that between water and sodium

$$2H_2O + 2Na \rightarrow 2NaOH + H_2$$
water                   sodium hydroxide

**Reaction with phosphorus pentachloride**   With phosphorus pentachloride, fumes of hydrogen chloride and phosphorus oxychloride are evolved.

$$C_2H_5OH + PCl_5 \rightarrow C_2H_5Cl + HCl + POCl_3$$

Compare this reaction with that between water and phosphorus pentachloride

$$H_2O + PCl_5 \rightarrow 2HCl + POCl_3$$

**Note**   This reaction with $PCl_5$ can be used to show the presence of a hydroxyl group in a compound.

The reactions involving ethanol are considerably less violent than those involving water. Can we account for this?

Both of the reactions involve a break up of the alcohol or water molecule between the oxygen atom and the hydrogen atom of the hydroxyl group.

Since the reaction involving ethanol is less violent, we must assume that this break up takes place less readily in the ethanol molecule. This can be accounted for if we assume that the alkyl part of the ethanol molecule repels the shared electrons towards the oxygen atom making it more difficult for the hydrogen atom to be released as a proton.

**Ester formation**   When warmed with organic acids, alcohols produce sweet smelling substances called **esters**.

$$CH_3COOH + C_2H_5OH \rightleftharpoons CH_3COOC_2H_5 + H_2O$$
ethanoic acid   ethanol          ethyl ethanoate

Esters will be considered in more detail later in this chapter.

**Dehydration**   When ethanol is warmed with an excess of concentrated sulphuric acid the product is ethene.

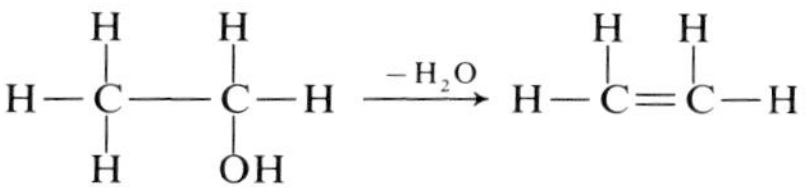

This process is often used for preparing ethene in the laboratory.

If there is insufficient acid present to give complete dehydration of the alcohol, then diethyl ether is formed.

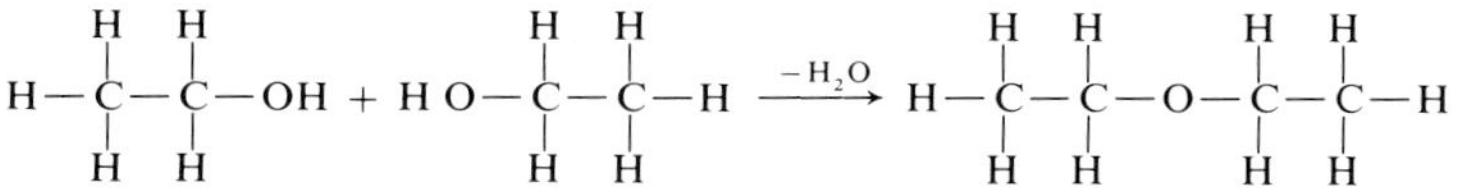

Diethyl ether is best known for its use as an anaesthetic.

**Oxidation of alcohols**   Alcohols burn in air to produce carbon dioxide and water.

$$C_2H_5OH + 3O_2 \rightarrow 2CO_2 + 3H_2O$$

Less severe oxidation, for example by heated copper(II) oxide or by acidified potassium dichromate(VI) solution, leads to a variety of products depending on the starting materials and the conditions of the reaction. Methanol is oxidized to methanal (formaldehyde) and then to methanoic acid (formic acid).

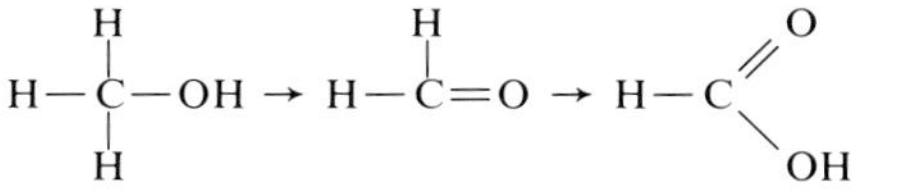

methanol        methanal        methanoic acid

Ethanol is oxidized to ethanal (acetaldehyde) and then to ethanoic acid (acetic acid).

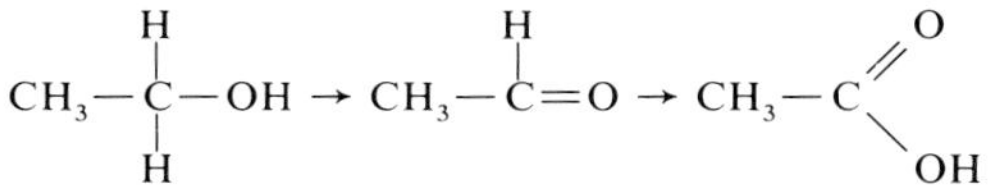

ethanol         ethanal         ethanoic acid

Methanol and ethanol are both examples of **primary alcohols**, that is alcohols in which the carbon bonded to the hydroxyl group is also bonded to two hydrogen atoms.

The oxidation of primary alcohols can be written as:

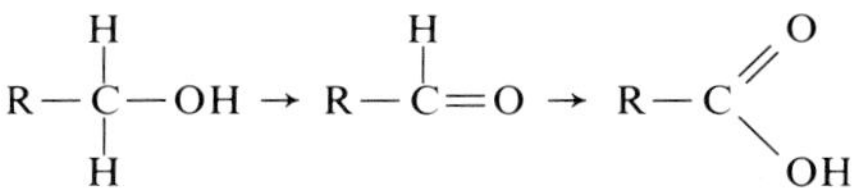

or

R.CH$_2$OH   $\rightarrow$   R.CHO   $\rightarrow$   R.COOH
primary alcohol        aldehyde    carboxylic acid

Propane-2-ol is oxidized to propanone (acetone) and further, more severe oxidation leads to a fragmentation of the molecule and the formation of a mixture of acids.

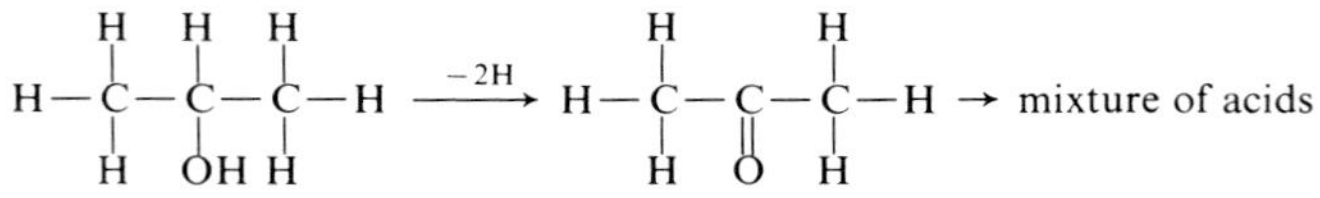

H—C—C—C—H $\xrightarrow{-2H}$ H—C—C—C—H → mixture of acids

propan-2-ol                    propanone

Propan-2-ol is an example of a **secondary alcohol,** that is an alcohol in which the carbon bonded to the hydroxyl group is only bonded to one hydrogen atom.

The oxidation of secondary alcohols can be written as:

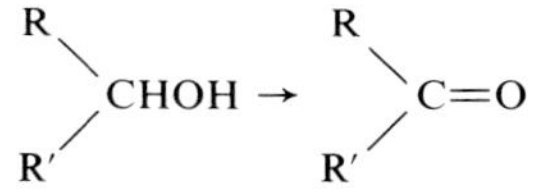

R
  \
    CHOH →
  /
R'
secondary
alcohol

R
  \
    C=O
  /
R'
ketone

2-methylpropan-2-ol is an example of a **tertiary alcohol**, one in which the carbon atom bonded to the hydroxyl group is not bonded to a hydrogen atom, but to three alkyl groups.

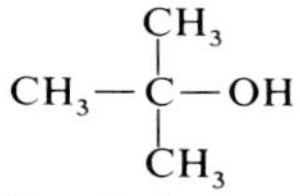

$$CH_3$$
$$CH_3—\overset{\displaystyle CH_3}{\underset{\displaystyle CH_3}{C}}—OH$$

2-methylpropan-2-ol

When tertiary alcohols are oxidized, they give rise to a mixture of ketones and acids.

**Phenol**

The formula for phenol (carbolic acid) is $C_6H_5OH$. It can be regarded as a benzene ring with one of the hydrogen atoms replaced by a hydroxyl group, and in many ways it undergoes the same reactions as benzene.

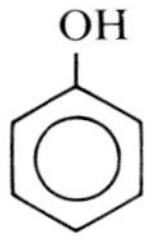

However it can also be regarded as a water molecule with one of the hydrogen atoms replaced by a phenyl group ($C_6H_5$), and as such it undergoes similar reactions to water and the alcohols which we have already considered.

Comparison with water

(a) With sodium on liquid phenol, hydrogen gas is evolved.

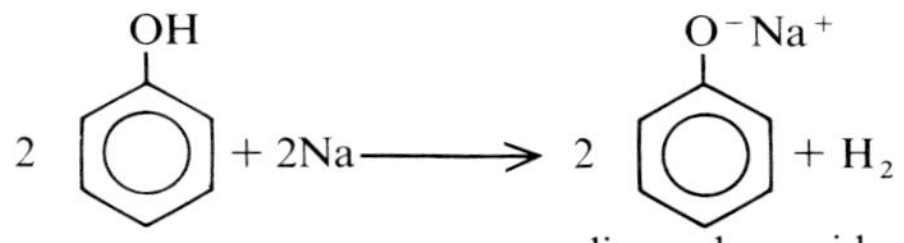

2 ⬡(OH) + 2Na ⟶ 2 ⬡(O⁻Na⁺) + H₂

sodium phenoxide

(b) With phosphorus pentachloride on liquid phenol, hydrogen chloride and phosphorus oxychloride are formed.

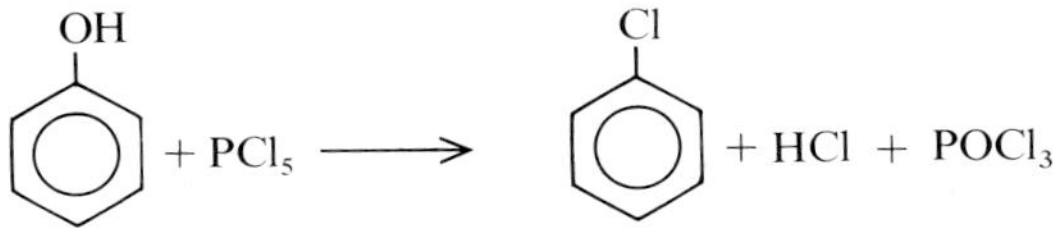

$$+ PCl_5 \longrightarrow \quad + HCl + POCl_3$$

**Acidic nature**   Unlike the alcohols we have considered, phenol ionizes slightly in aqueous solution to produce hydrogen ions.

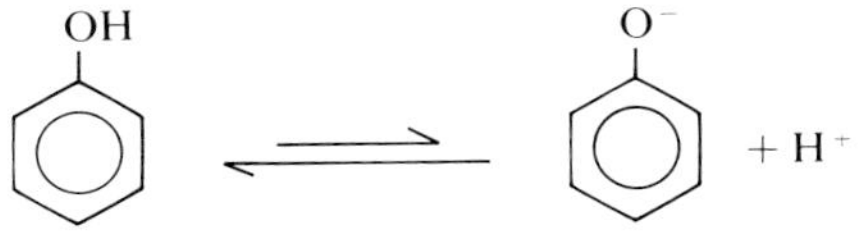

$$\rightleftharpoons \quad + H^+$$

Phenol is a very weak acid, which will not liberate carbon dioxide from sodium carbonate but it will undergo the following typical reactions:

1   It reacts with bases to form salts.

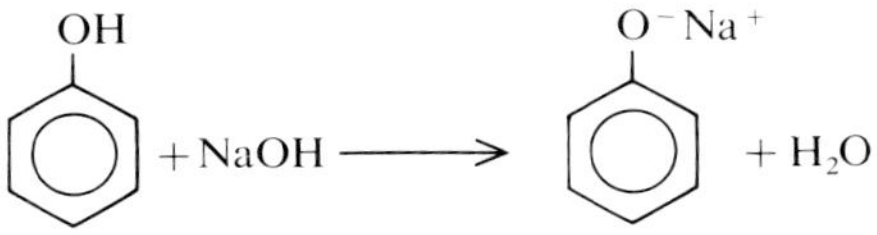

$$+ NaOH \longrightarrow \quad + H_2O$$

2   It is displaced from its salts by stronger acids.

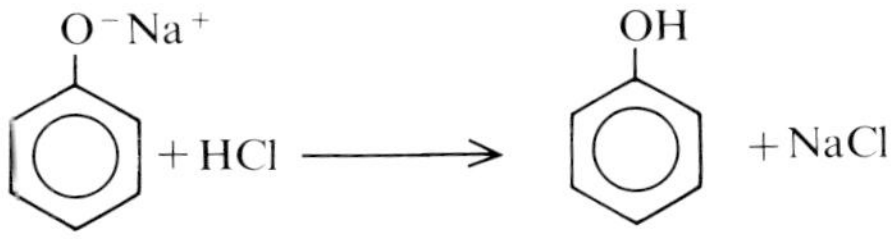

$$+ HCl \longrightarrow \quad + NaCl$$

The ionization of the phenol molecule can be accounted for if we assume that the benzene ring attracts the shared electrons making it easier for the oxygen-hydrogen bond to break.

3   It reacts with chlorine water to form trichlorphenol (T.C.P.).

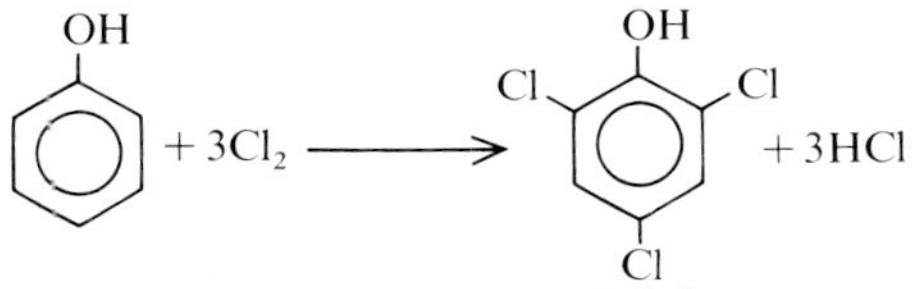

$$+ 3Cl_2 \longrightarrow \quad + 3HCl$$

T.C.P.

**Uses**   The characteristic odour of phenol can be recognized in many of the phenol products on the market, for example in carbolic soap. Phenol was one of the first antiseptics to be used by the medical profession. Other important products include dyes and drugs.

**Dihydric and trihydric alcohols**

Dihydric alcohols contain two hydroxyl groups. The most common dihydric alcohol is ethane-1,2-diol (ethylene glycol), prepared by the oxidation of ethene.

$$
\begin{array}{c}
\text{H} \\
| \\
\text{H}-\text{C}-\text{OH} \\
| \\
\text{H}-\text{C}-\text{OH} \\
| \\
\text{H}
\end{array}
$$

Trihydric alcohols have three hydroxyl groups. The most common trihydric alcohol is propane-1,2,3-triol (glycerol).

$$
\begin{array}{c}
\text{H} \\
| \\
\text{H}-\text{C}-\text{OH} \\
| \\
\text{H}-\text{C}-\text{OH} \\
| \\
\text{H}-\text{C}-\text{OH} \\
| \\
\text{H}
\end{array}
$$

Large quantities of glycerol are obtained as a by-product in the manufacture of soap.

The hydroxyl groups in dihydric and trihydric alcohols behave in a similar fashion to the hydroxyl groups in monohydric alcohols.

## 9.2  Aldehydes and ketones

**Introduction**

Aldehydes and ketones both have a carbonyl group in their molecules. In aldehydes there is a hydrogen atom and an alkyl group attached to this carbonyl group.

$$
\begin{array}{c}
\text{R} \\
\diagdown \\
\phantom{xx}\text{C}=\text{O} \\
\diagup \\
\text{H}
\end{array}
$$

In ketones there are two alkyl groups attached to the carbonyl group.

$$
\begin{array}{c}
\text{R} \\
\diagdown \\
\phantom{xx}\text{C}=\text{O} \\
\diagup \\
\text{R}'
\end{array}
$$

Table 9.3 gives the names and formulae of some aldehydes and ketones.

**Table 9.3**

| Aldehydes | | Ketones | |
|-----------|------|---------|------|
| Formula | Name | Formula | Name |
| $HCHO$ | methanal | $(CH_3)_2CO$ | propanone |
| $CH_3CHO$ | ethanal | $CH_3COC_2H_5$ | butanone |
| $C_2H_5CHO$ | propanal | $C_2H_5COC_2H_5$ | pentan-3-one |

**Similarities between aldehydes and ketones**

Due to the fact that aldehydes and ketones both contain the carbonyl group, they have many properties in common.

**1**    Condensation reactions with hydrazines

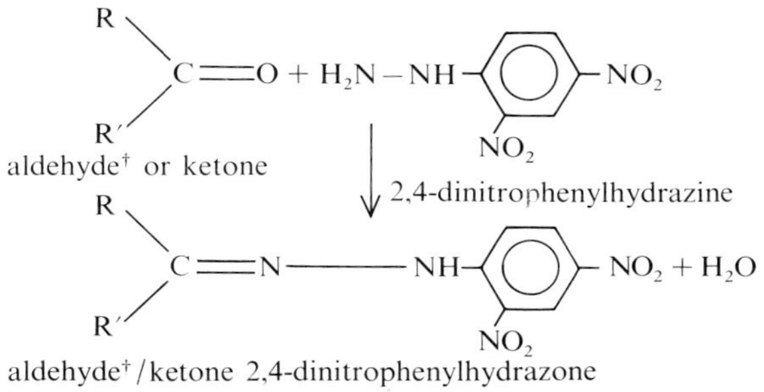

Unknown aldehydes and ketones are identified by preparing the hydrazone derivative, a crystalline compound, and comparing its melting point with the melting points of known compounds.

**2**    Addition reaction with sodium hydrogen sulphite

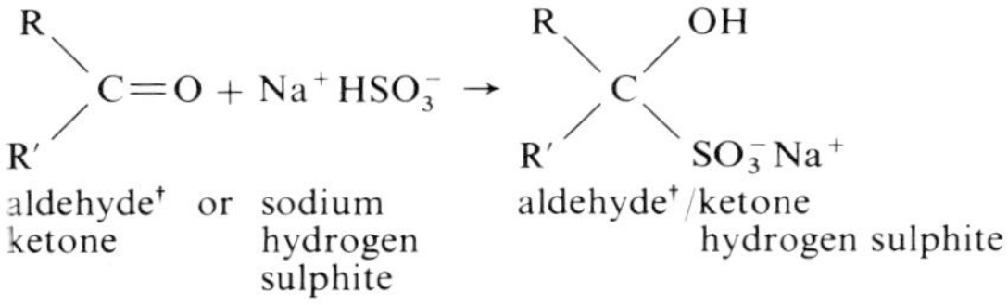

Addition reactions of this type make useful identification tests for compounds containing the carbonyl group.

**3**    Reduction by hydrogen

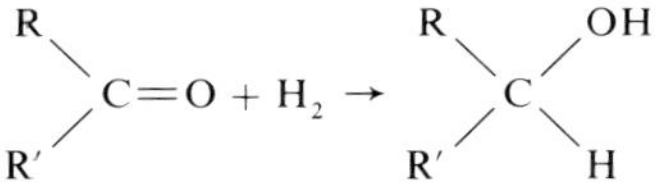

When a ketone is reduced the product is a secondary alcohol and when an aldehyde is reduced the product is a primary alcohol.

**Distinguishing tests for aldehydes and ketones**    Aldehydes show reducing properties which the ketones do not, and they can be distinguished by treating them with oxidizing agents as follows. Aldehydes may be oxidized to carboxylic acids by the following oxidizing agents:

**1**    Acidified dichromate solution

$$Cr_2O_7^{2-} + 14H^+ + 6e^- \rightarrow 2Cr^{3+} + 7H_2O \qquad \text{reduction}$$
orange                          green

**2**    Fehling's solution (alkaline $Cu^{2+}$ solution)

$$2Cu^{2+}(aq) + H_2O + 2e^- \rightarrow Cu_2O(s) + 2H^+ \qquad \text{reduction}$$
blue                          red

† $R' = H$ in the case of an aldehyde.

3    Tollens' reagent (ammoniacal $Ag^+NO_3^-$ solution)

$Ag^+ + e^- \rightarrow Ag$                                    reduction
colourless      silver mirror forms

## 9.3 Carboxylic Acids

**Introduction**    Every member of the homologous series of carboxylic acids contains the

functional group $-C\overset{\displaystyle O}{\underset{\displaystyle OH}{\diagup}}$   which is known as the carboxylic acid group.

Table 9.4 gives the names of formulae of the first few members of this series.

**Table 9.4**

| Name | Formula |
| --- | --- |
| methanoic acid | $HCOOH$ |
| ethanoic acid | $CH_3COOH$ |
| propanoic acid | $C_2H_5COOH$ |
| butanoic acid | $C_3H_7COOH$ |

Carboxylic acids can be prepared by oxidation of the corresponding alcohol or aldehyde.

$\underset{\text{ethanol}}{C_2H_5OH} \rightarrow \underset{\text{ethanoic acid}}{CH_3COOH} + H_2O$

$\underset{\text{ethanal}}{CH_3CHO} \rightarrow \underset{\text{ethanoic acid}}{CH_3COOH}$

**Properties**    The carboxylic acids display all the characteristic properties of acids:

1    Reaction with sodium.

$2Na + 2CH_3COOH \rightarrow H_2 + 2CH_3COONa$

2    Neutralization by bases.

$CH_3COOH + NaOH \rightarrow CH_3COONa + H_2O$

3    Reaction with carbonates.

$2CH_3COOH + Na_2CO_3 \rightarrow CH_3COONa + H_2O + CO_2$

4    They are weak acids, only partially ionizing in aqueous solution.

$CH_3COOH(l) + H_2O(l) \rightleftharpoons CH_3COO^-(aq) + H_3O^+(aq)$

The constitution of ethanoic acid is not so simple as the formula might suggest. Reaction with chlorine yields trichloroethanoic acid and this establishes the presence of the methyl group. Reaction with $PCl_5$ establishes the presence of the hydroxyl group. However, ethanoic acid does not form addition compounds with 2,4-dinitrophenylhydrazine: this indicates that there is no carbonyl group present. Table 9.5 shows the C—O bond length in various forms.

**Table 9.5**

| Bond | Bond length in nm |
|---|---|
| C—O (alcohol) | 0.143 |
| C=O (ketone) | 0.122 |
| C—O (acid) | 0.130 |

The behaviour of the 'carbonyl group' is influenced by the presence of the hydroxyl group since both oxygen atoms are bonded to the same carbon atom and delocalization of electrons is possible.

$$\left[ CH_3-C \begin{array}{c} O \\ \\ O \end{array} \right]^{-} \quad H^+$$

For most purposes the conventional formula, although incorrect, will be good enough.

$$CH_3-C \begin{array}{c} O \\ \\ OH \end{array}$$

### 9.4  Esters

**Preparation**   Esters may be prepared by refluxing a mixture of the carboxylic acid and the alcohol in the presence of concentrated sulphuric acid. This process is called **esterification**.

$$HCOOH + C_2H_5OH \rightleftharpoons HCOOC_2H_5 + H_2O$$
methanoic   ethanol                  ethyl
acid                                 methanoate

$$CH_3COOH + CH_3OH \rightleftharpoons CH_3COOCH_3 + H_2O$$
ethanoic   methanol               methyl
acid                               ethanoate

The function of the concentrated sulphuric acid is to displace the equilibrium to the right by removing the water which is formed.

In an acid/alkali neutralization reaction, the acid provides the hydrogen ion, and the alkali provides the hydroxide ion for the formation of water.

$$\boxed{H^+}\,Cl^-(aq) + Na^+\boxed{OH^-}(aq) \rightarrow Na^+Cl^-(aq) + H_2O(l)$$

In the acid/alcohol esterification reaction, there would appear to be two possible mechanisms for the production of water since both the acid and the alcohol contain a hydroxyl group.

Methanol is prepared using an isotope of oxygen $^{18}O$. Ethanoic acid and methanol are refluxed with concentrated sulphuric acid to produce the ester methyl ethanoate and water. The products are separated by distillation and examined for the presence of $^{18}O$ in the mass spectrometer.

Only the ester is found to contain this isotope, so the correct mechanism for the reaction is

**Hydrolysis**   If esters are refluxed with water, equilibrium is reached and the products contain the appropriate acid and alcohol

$$CH_3COOC_5H_{11} + H_2O \rightleftharpoons CH_3COOH + C_5H_{11}OH$$
pentyl ethanoate                    ethanoic acid   pentanol
'Pear drops'

This reaction is called **hydrolysis** since it involves reaction with water. For practical purposes it is more satisfactory to hydrolyze esters by refluxing with a dilute alkali such as sodium hydroxide solution. In this case the products are the sodium salt of the carboxylic acid and the alcohol.

$$CH_3COOCH_3 + NaOH \rightarrow CH_3COONa + CH_3OH$$
methyl                    sodium                    methanol
ethanoate                 ethanoate

This process is widely used in the preparation of soap.

The naturally occurring ester glyceryl tristearate, found in animal fat, is hydrolyzed by boiling with a dilute alkali to produce the sodium salt of stearic acid, soap. The process is called **saponification**.

propane-1,2,3-trioctadecanoate                    propane-1,2,3,-triol

Brine is then added to separate or 'salt-out' the soap which can be skimmed from the surface of the mixture, purified, compressed and dried to give the final product.

## 9.5 Amines

**Introduction**   Amines are organic compounds which contain the amino group —$NH_2$ in their molecular structure. Table 9.5 gives the names and formulae of the first few members of the amine series.

**Table 9.5**

| Name | Formula |
| --- | --- |
| methylamine | $CH_3NH_2$ |
| ethylamine | $C_2H_5NH_2$ |
| propylamine | $C_3H_7NH_2$ |
| butylamine | $C_4H_9NH_2$ |

The structure of amines can be pictured as ammonia molecules with one of the hydrogen atoms replaced by an alkyl group.

ammonia     amine

The amines which have been considered so far are primary amines. If we picture the ammonia molecule with two or three hydrogen atoms replaced by alkyl groups, then we have examples of secondary or tertiary amines respectively.

primary amine     secondary amine     tertiary amine

## Properties of amines

1   The properties of amines are similar to those of ammonia. They have a characteristic 'fish-like' odour.

2   They dissolve in water to give alkaline solutions.

ethylamine     ethyl ammonium hydroxide

3   They are neutralized by acids to give salts.

$$C_2H_5NH_2 + HCl \rightarrow C_2H_5NH_3^+Cl^-$$
ethylamine                    ethylamine hydrochloride

4   Their salts react with strong alkalis to give the free amine.

$$C_2H_5NH_3^+Cl^- + NaOH \rightarrow C_2H_5NH_2 + H_2O + NaCl$$
ethylamine                    ethylamine
hydrochloride

5   They form complex ions with copper(II) sulphate solution.

$$Cu^{2+}SO_4^{2-}(aq) + 4C_2H_5NH_2 \rightarrow [Cu(C_2H_5NH_2)_4]^{2+}SO_4^{2-}$$
                                        copper ethylammonium sulphate
                                        dark blue

c.f.   $$Cu^{2+}SO_4^{2-}(aq) + 4NH_3 \rightarrow [Cu(NH_3)_4]^{2+}SO_4^{2-}$$
                                        copper ammonium sulphate
                                        dark blue

**Aniline**   Aniline (or phenylamine) has the formula $C_6H_5NH_2$. It is an ammonia molecule with one of the hydrogen atoms replaced by a benzene ring

phenylamine

Phenylamine exhibits all the basic properties of ethylamine, but to a lesser degree. Why should it be less basic?

In section 9.16 we assumed that the benzene ring was electron attracting and used this assumption to account for the acidic nature of phenol $C_6H_5OH$.

If we once again assume that the benzene ring is electron attracting, then the result will be that the lone pair of electrons on the nitrogen are not so readily available for accepting protons, hence the less basic nature of phenylamine in comparison with ammonia. Similarly if we assume that alkyl groups are electron repelling, then the result will be that the electrons are more available for accepting protons and that alkyl amines are stronger bases than ammonia. It also follows that secondary alkyl amines are stronger bases than primary alkyl amines and that tertiary alkyl amines are stronger bases than secondary amines.

## 9.6 Amino-acids and proteins

**Amino-acids**   Amino-acids are carboxylic acids with one of the hydrogen atoms of the alkyl groups replaced by an amino group.

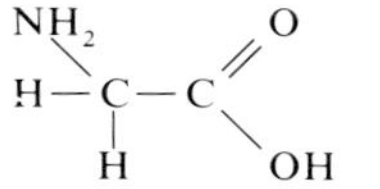

aminoethanoic acid (glycine)

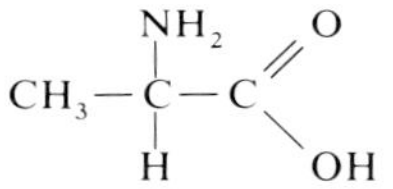

2-amino propanoic acid (alanine)

Amino-acid molecules have both basic and acidic functional groups present and the resultant character depends on the relative numbers of these groups. Due to the presence of these groups, amino-acid molecules can react with each other.

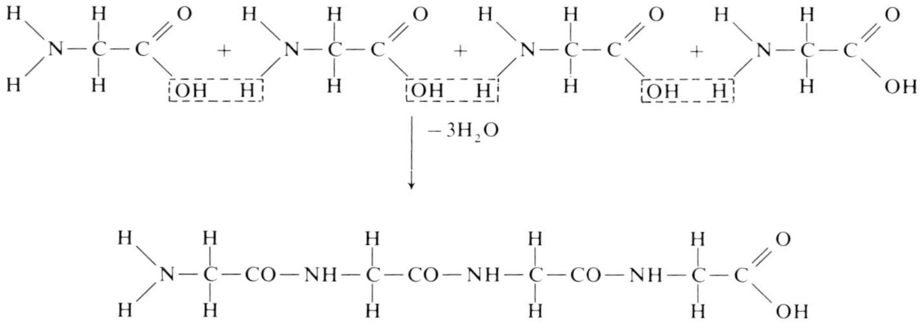

$-3H_2O$

protein-like molecule

The reaction is a **condensation reaction** and the link formed between the two molecules is called a **peptide link**.

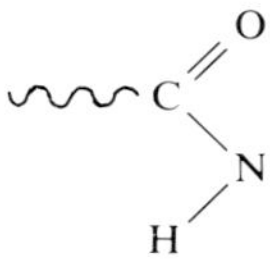

peptide link

**Proteins**    Proteins are formed by large numbers of $\alpha$-amino-acid molecules linking in this way to form polymers with molecular masses greater than 10 000.
An $a$-amino-acid is one in which both functional groups are attached to the same carbon atom.

There are about 24 'essential' $a$-amino acids, but because they can link together in thousands of different ways, there are thousands of different proteins. They do, however, have the same basic backbone, a chain of peptide links, often referred to as a **peptide chain**.

$$-(P)-\underset{\underset{O}{\parallel}}{C}-\underset{\underset{H}{|}}{N}-(Q)-\underset{\underset{O}{\parallel}}{C}-\underset{\underset{H}{|}}{N}-(R)-\underset{\underset{O}{\parallel}}{C}-\underset{\underset{H}{|}}{N}-(S)-\underset{\underset{O}{\parallel}}{C}-\underset{\underset{H}{|}}{N}-(T)-\underset{\underset{O}{\parallel}}{C}-\underset{\underset{H}{|}}{N}-(U)-$$

peptide link    peptide link    peptide link    peptide link    peptide link

where P, Q, R, S, T, U can represent different amino-acids.

Proteins taken into the body are digested into their constituent amino-acids—a hydrolysis process involving specific enzymes. The amino-acid molecules are small enough to pass into the bloodstream and so they can be carried to any part of the body, wherever they are needed to be reformed into body protein.

**Summary**

From this chapter you should know:

1  The meaning of the term functional group.

2  That the alcohols exhibit isomerism.

3  The methods of preparation and properties of the alcohols.

4  How to test for the hydroxyl group.

5  The reactions of phenol.

6  The methods of preparation and properties of aldehydes and ketones.

7  How to distinguish between an aldehyde and a ketone.

8  The methods of preparation and properties of carboxylic acids.

9  The structure of the carboxylic acid group.

10  The method of preparation and properties of esters.

11  How to establish the mechanism of the esterification reaction.

12  The properties of the amines and their similarity to ammonia.

13  The structure of amino-acids.

14  How amino-acids link to form proteins.

**Questions on chapters 8 and 9**

1    The following table gives information about the addition of bromine to four different hydrocarbons.

|   | Molecular formula of hydrocarbon | Addition compound formed on reaction with bromine |
|---|---|---|
| A | $C_6H_{12}$ | $C_6H_{12}Br_2$ |
| B | $C_6H_{12}$ | No addition product formed |
| C | $C_6H_{10}$ | $C_6H_{10}Br_4$ |
| D | $C_6H_{10}$ | $C_6H_{10}Br_2$ |

Draw a possible structural formula for each of the hydrocarbons $A$, $B$, $C$ and $D$. *SCEEB*

2

$$C_3H_6 \xrightarrow{\textcircled{1}} C_3H_7Br \xrightarrow{\textcircled{2}} C_3H_7OH \xrightarrow{\textcircled{3}} C_3H_6O$$
$$\;\;A \qquad\qquad B \qquad\qquad C \qquad\qquad D$$

The above reaction scheme outlines the conversion of an alkene $A$ to a ketone $D$.
1    Draw structural formulae for $A$, $B$, $C$, and $D$.
2    Name the type of change which takes place at ①, ②, and ③ respectively.
3    State the reagent and conditions for the reaction at ②.
4    Outline how $C$ could be changed back to $A$.
5    What, if anything, would be observed on addition of
    **5.1**    silver nitrate solution to $B$,
    **5.2**    bromine water to $A$,
    **5.3**    sodium    to    $C$?
6    When $A$ is heated under pressure in the presence of a titanium catalyst, it polymerizes to form a useful plastic material $E$.
Name $E$, and make a diagram showing its structure. (At least *three* monomer units should be shown). *SCEEB*

3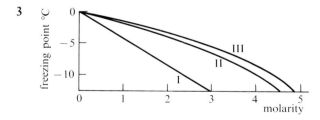

    I—sodium chloride
  II—ethane-1,2-diol
III—ethanol

The above graph shows the freezing point curves for solutions of different concentrations of the three substances sodium chloride, ethane-1,2-diol (ethylene glycol) and ethanol.

The following table gives the boiling points of ethane, ethanol, and ethane-1,2-diol.

| ethane | −89 °C |
| ethanol | 78 °C |
| ethane-1,2-diol | 198 °C |

**1**   Ethane-1,2-diol is a dihydric alcohol. What is meant by the term dihydric? Write the structural formula of ethane-1,2-diol.
**2**   Ethane-1,2-diol is used as an antifreeze for car cooling systems, yet from the graph it would appear that sodium chloride is more efficient. Why is ethane-1,2-diol preferred to sodium chloride?
**3**   From the graph, ethanol and ethane-1,2-diol would appear to be almost equally effective as antifreezes; suggest one property of ethane-1,2-diol which makes it preferable for this purpose.
**4**   A man discovers that the lowest temperature ever recorded in his area is −10 °C. What is the least weight of ethane-1,2-diol he should use in each litre of solution to provide protection for his car cooling system?
**5**   A first-year pupil has mixed salt and ice in a beaker and has seen that the temperature falls. He is therefore puzzled when he sees salt being thrown on an icy road 'to melt the ice'. What explanation would you give him as to why this is done?
**6**   What information can be obtained from the boiling points about the forces of attraction *between* molecules of ethane, ethane-1,2-diol and ethanol? Outline the accepted theory which accounts for this.
On the basis of the theory how would you account for the following facts:
    ethanol is much less viscous than ethane-1,2-diol;
    ethanol and ethane-1,2-diol are both completely miscible with water, whereas ethane is practically insoluble in water? *SCEEB*

**4**   The following instructions for the preparation of ethyl ethanoate (ethyl acetate) are given in a book on practical organic chemistry.
'A mixture of 12 g of glacial acetic acid (i.e. 100% acetic acid) and 9 g of absolute alcohol (i.e. 100% ethanol) is added drop by drop at the same speed as the liquid distils to a mixture of 8 g of concentrated sulphuric acid and 4 g of absolute alcohol in a distilling flask attached to a condenser and receiver and heated in an oil bath at 140 °C. The distillate is shaken with sodium carbonate solution until the upper layer is no longer acid to moist litmus paper. This layer is shaken with calcium chloride and then allowed to stand for 24 hours over calcium chloride. It is filtered through a dry filter paper, and fractionated on a water bath, the fraction coming over at 73–80° being redistilled.'
**1**   To what group of substances does ethyl ethanoate (ethyl acetate) belong? Write its formula.
**2**   Make a sketch of the apparatus used in the first stage of the above experiment, in which the crude compound is obtained.
**3**   What is likely to happen when the crude distillate is shaken with sodium carbonate solution and why?
**4**   Write the equation for the formation of ethyl ethanoate (ethyl acetate) in the above reaction.
**5**   What part does the sulphuric acid play in the process?

**6** What is the purpose of allowing the substance to stand over calcium chloride?
**7** What is meant by the term 'fractionated'?
**8** The yield obtained in the above experiment was 13 g. Calculate the maximum weight of ethyl ethanoate (ethyl acetate) obtainable from 12 g of acetic acid, and the percentage yield. Why is it not 100%? *SCEEB*

**5** What is meant by a polar molecule?
   **1** Write the formula of one substance which has polar molecules and one which has not.
   **2** Benzene has the formula $C_6H_6$. Draw a possible open-chain structure which could be represented by this formula, and describe *one* reaction of benzene which would lead you to suspect that the formula you have drawn is not a correct one for benzene.
   **3** Outline a chemical method of distinguishing the three hydroxyl compounds hydroxybenzene (phenol), ethanol, and sodium hydroxide. (The same test must be applied to each compound.)
   **4** Aniline and ethylamine are both amines, but they differ very much in strength as bases.
What group is common to both these compounds?
Which is the stronger base?
By considering the properties of phenol and ethanol, state what effect the introduction of a $C_6H_5$— group into a molecule in place of $C_2H_5$— has on the acidic or basic properties of the compound.
   **5** Proteins may be considered as polymers of amino-acids. Give the structural formula of a typical amino-acid, and show how three such units are linked to form part of a protein molecule.
   **6** How would you show that a protein contains nitrogen and hydrogen? *SCEEB*

**6**   **1** What is meant by the terms
     **1.1** homologous series,
     **1.2** isomerism?
   **2** From the Heats of Combustion in Data table E1 (page 190) choose values for the *three* members of each of *two* homologous series. Use these figures to support the statement.
'There is a regular increase in the heat of combustion as you move up a homologous series. The increase is the same for all such series.'
Give a name for each of the two series you choose.
   **3** There are four isomeric alcohols of molecular formula $C_4H_9OH$. Their structural formulae are as follows:

$CH_3CH_2CH_2CH_2OH$  (I)            $CH_3CH_2\underset{\underset{OH}{|}}{C}HCH_3$  (II)

$CH_3-\underset{\underset{OH}{|}}{\overset{\overset{CH_3}{|}}{C}}-CH_3$  (III)        $CH_3\underset{\underset{CH_3}{}}{\overset{\overset{CH_3}{|}}{C}}HCH_2OH$  (IV)

     **3.1** Give systematic names for (I), (II), (III), and (IV).
     **3.2** State which of the compounds I–IV are primary, which secondary, and which tertiary alcohols.
     **3.3** The four alcohols are contained, separately, in four bottles

marked *A*, *B*, *C*, and *D*. From the following information decide which bottle contains which alcohol. State your reasoning briefly at each stage.

(a) The contents of *A*, *B*, and *C* can readily be oxidized by acid potassium dichromate solution, while those of *D* cannot.

(b) *A* and *B*, on complete oxidation by the dichromate, give acids of formulae $C_3H_7COOH$.
*C* does not give this acid.

(c) All four substances can be dehydrated to give alkenes. *A* and *D* can both form the same alkene. *B* and *C* can both form the same alkene, which is an isomer of that formed by *A* and *D*. *SCEEB*

7   Ethanol is produced by reacting steam with ethene in the presence of a catalyst according to the equation

$$C_2H_4(g) + H_2O(g) \rightleftharpoons C_2H_5OH(g)$$

Under practical conditions only 10% of the ethene is converted.

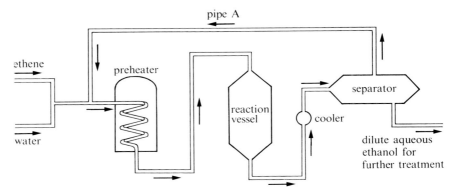

1   Would a high or low pressure in the reaction vessel favour the production of ethanol?
2   What is flowing in pipe A?
3   On what principle does the separation in the separator depend?
4   What further treatment would be necessary to obtain more concentrated ethanol? *SCEEB*

8   Demand for the element nickel (Ni, atomic number 28) is increasing each year. Nickel is used in the hydrogenation of vegetable oils to produce fats. This is carried out as follows. The oil is heated to 180 °C along with finely divided nickel. Hydrogen gas is passed in under 5 atmosphere pressure.
**1.1**   A typical vegetable oil can be represented by the structure

where ■■ represent hydrocarbon chains.
To which class of organic compounds does the oil belong?
**1.2**   Draw the molecule which will be produced by the hydrogenation of the vegetable oil.
**1.3**   Given a sample from the reaction vessel, how would you discover if hydrogenation was complete?

**1.4**   What part does the nickel play in the hydrogenation process?
**1.5**   Why should it be 'finely divided'? *SCEEB*

**9**   Ethanol has the extended structural formula

$$H-\overset{\overset{\displaystyle H}{|}}{\underset{\underset{\displaystyle H}{|}}{C}}-\overset{\overset{\displaystyle H}{|}}{\underset{\underset{\displaystyle H}{|}}{C}}-O-H$$

Write such a formula for
**1**   propan-1-ol
**2**   propanal
**3**   propanoic acid. *SCEEB*

**10**   **1**   Draw the extended structural formula for but-1-yne.
**2**   Draw the extended structural formula for an isomer of but-1-yne.
*SCEEB*

**11**   **1**   ethanol; ethanal; glycerol (propane-1,2,3-triol.)
Decide which of the above would show evidence of the strongest hydrogen bonding and justify your choice.
**2**   A pupil mixes 50 ml ethanol with 50 ml benzene (both liquids at 20 °C) and observes a slight fall in temperature on mixing.
He mixes 50 ml ethanol with 50 ml water (both liquids at 20 °C) and observes a slight rise in temperature on mixing.
Account for these observations in terms of the possible extent of hydrogen bonding before and after mixing. *SCEEB*

**12**   Parts **1**, **2**, **3**, and **4** refer to the following reaction sequence:

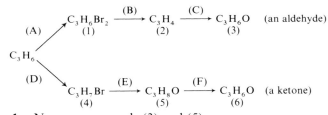

**1**   Name compounds (3) and (5).
**2**   Draw structural formulae of (3), (6), (1) and (4).
**3**   What reagents would achieve steps (A), (D), (E) and (F)?
**4**   Describe a test which would distinguish between the isomeric compounds (3) and (6).
**5**   An ester can be made by the reaction of methanol with propanoic acid.
  **5.1**   Draw the structural formula of the ester and give its name.
  **5.2**   State *briefly* how you would carry out the reaction. How would you ensure that it went to completion? *SCEEB*

**13**

| Acid | Formula | Strength |
|---|---|---|
| trifluoroethanoic | $CF_3COOH$ | strong |
| trichloroethanoic | $CCl_3COOH$ | ↑ |
| dichloroethanoic | $CHCl_2COOH$ | |
| monochloroethanoic | $CH_2ClCOOH$ | |
| ethanoic | $CH_3COOH$ | weak |

The table shows some acids arranged in order of acid strength.

**1**    What is the effect of halogen substitution on the strength of ethanoic acid?

**2**    Under similar conditions which of the chlorine substituted compounds would be the best conductor of electricity?

**3**    Deduce the strength of tri-iodoethanoic acid relative to that of trichloroethanoic acid.

**4**    Write a balanced equation for the action of trifluoroethanoic acid on magnesium. *SCEEB*

**14**

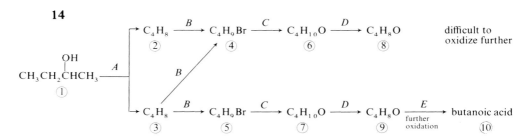

**1**    Is compound ① a primary, secondary or tertiary alcohol?

**2**    Draw structural formulae for the isomeric compounds ② and ③.

**3**    What reagents would be used in steps *A, B, C* and *E*?

**4**    Draw structural formulae for ⑧ and ⑨ and name a reagent (other than *E*) which you could use to distinguish between them.

**5**    Which of compounds ⑥ and ⑦ is an isomer of ①?

**6**    Which compound ④, ⑥ or ⑧ would react with sodium to produce hydrogen?

**7**    Experiment shows that butanoic acid has a formula weight of approximately twice the expected value. Offer an explanation.

**8**    Draw the structural formula for the ester formed by the action of ① and ⑩.

**9**    When substance ① is mixed with water, there is a slight increase in temperature, but when ① is mixed with cyclohexane, $C_6H_{12}$, there is a slight decrease in temperature. Explain these observations with reference to the breaking and making of hydrogen bonds. *SCEEB*

**15**

**1**    $CH_3CH_2OH \xrightarrow{\text{heated aluminium oxide}} A$

**2**    $CH_3CH_2$
       $\phantom{xxxxx}\diagdown$
       $\phantom{xxxxxxx}CHOH \xrightarrow{\text{heated copper(II) oxide}} B$
       $\phantom{xxxxx}\diagup$
       $CH_3CH_2$

**3**    $CH_3COOH + CH_3CH_2CH_2OH \xrightarrow{\text{reflux with acid}} C$

Write down the structural formulae of the organic products A, B, and C. *SCEEB*

# Experimental section

**Chapter 3**

**Experiment 1**    Determination of the formula weight of a gas
Weigh an 'empty' butane lighter-fuel cylinder, which is fitted with a
re-sealable rubber cap.
Using a 50 cm³ syringe, carefully place 150 cm³ of methane gas in the
cylinder.
Reweigh the cylinder.
Copy and complete the table of results.

Mass of cylinder + 150 cm³ methane =    g

Mass of cylinder 'empty'        =    g

Mass of methane           =    g

Volume of methane        = 150 cm³

Calculate the mass of gas which occupies 22.4 l (Ignore the correction
to s.t.p.)

**Experiment 2**    Determination of the formula weight of a gas.
Set up the apparatus shown in the diagram.

Use the vacuum pump to remove as much air as possible from the flask.
Weigh the flask. Flush it with carbon dioxide gas and reweigh it.
Determine the volume of the apparatus by filling it with water and
measuring the volume of water.
Repeat the experiment with sulphur dioxide, nitrogen and oxygen.
Calculate the mass of gas which occupies 22.4 l. (Ignore the correction
to s.t.p.)
*Note* A hand pump or a water pump will give a reasonable vacuum.
There is a danger of implosion if a high vacuum pump is used.

**Experiment 3**    Consider the equation:

$$Mg(s) \; + \; 2HCl(aq) \; \rightarrow \; MgCl_2(aq) + H_2(g)$$
1 mole     2 moles       1 mole       1 mole
24.3 g     2 litres 1M    1 litre 1M    22.4 l at s.t.p.

The equation shows that 1 mole of magnesium reacts with 2 moles of
hydrochloric acid to produce 1 mole of magnesium chloride solution and
1 mole of hydrogen gas.

Accurately weigh about 0.02 g of magnesium.

Place 4 cm³ of 1M hydrochloric acid in a test tube, tilt the tube to one side and place a piece of magnesium on the side of the tube so that it does not fall into the acid. Attach the tube to a 100 cm³ ground glass syringe. Tilt the tube so that the magnesium falls into the acid.

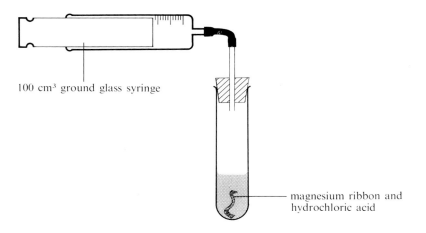

100 cm³ ground glass syringe

magnesium ribbon and hydrochloric acid

The hydrogen gas evolved will push the plunger of the syringe out. When the reaction has ceased, measure the volume of hydrogen. Copy and complete the table of results

Weight of magnesium          =        g

Volume of hydrogen gas evolved =        cm³

1   What is the ratio
(moles of magnesium):(moles of hydrogen gas) produced?

2   How does your result compare with the equation obtained from theoretical conditions?

**Experiment 4**   Determination of the formula weight of a volatile liquid.

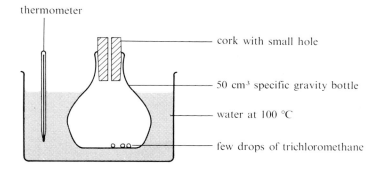

thermometer

cork with small hole

50 cm³ specific gravity bottle

water at 100 °C

few drops of trichloromethane

Weigh the density bottle full of air to the nearest milligram. Fill it with water and reweigh it. Calculate the volume of the density bottle to the nearest cm³. Measure the atmospheric pressure.

Empty the flask and dry it. Put a few drops of trichloromethane (chloroform) in the density bottle and place it in a beaker of boiling water until the drops of trichloromethane disappear. Remove the density bottle from the water-bath, dry it carefully, cool and weigh it to the nearest milligram.

Copy and complete the following table of results:

Mass of density bottle 'empty'                            =        g

Mass of density bottle + water                           =        g

Mass of density bottle + trichloromethane  =        g

Mass of trichloromethane                                   =        g

Pressure =        mm Hg

Volume of water =        cm$^3$ = volume of gas at 373 K

1   Calculate the volume of trichloromethane at s.t.p. assuming it was a gas.
2   Calculate the mass of trichloromethane which occupies 22.4 l at s.t.p.
3   Explain why some weighings are more accurately determined than others.
4   Justify ignoring the mass of the air in this experiment.

**Experiment 5**   Set up the apparatus shown on page 31, Figure 3.4, and measure a current for a time which gives easily measured volumes of gas.
Attempt to reproduce Table 3.1.

## Chapter 4

In all the following experiments it is assumed that all the solutions will be at the same initial temperature (room temperature).

**Experiment 1**   Endothermic and exothermic reactions.

Place 20 cm$^3$ of water in each of two boiling tubes. Record the temperature in each tube.
To one tube add 0.5 g of solid sodium hydroxide, stir, record the temperature and calculate the temperature change.
To the second tube add 0.5 g of solid ammonium nitrate, stir, record the temperature and calculate the temperature change.
From your results, say which reaction is exothermic and which is endothermic, and offer an explanation in terms of bond-breaking and bond-making.

**Experiment 2**   Verification of Hess's Law.

Aqueous sodium chloride can be produced from solid sodium hydroxide by two different routes. By measuring all the temperature changes in each route it will be possible to show that the enthalpy change is the same regardless of the path taken.

1   Place 100 cm$^3$ of 1M hydrochloric acid in a thermos flask and record the temperature. Add 4 g of solid sodium hydroxide, stir and record the highest temperature observed.

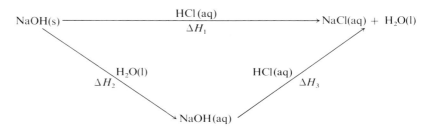

2   Place 100 cm³ of water in a thermos flask and record the temperature. Add 4 g of solid sodium hydroxide and stir. Record the highest temperature observed.

3   Place 100 cm³ of sodium hydroxide solution and 100 cm³ of 1M hydrochloric acid in separate thermos flasks. Record the temperature in each flask. Add the acid to the alkali and record the highest temperature observed. Using the equation $\Delta H = c \times m \times \Delta T$, calculate $\Delta H_1$, $\Delta H_2$ and $\Delta H_3$ and use the values obtained to verify Hess's Law.

**Experiment 3**   Heat of neutralization.

1   Place 100 cm³ of 1M sodium hydroxide solution and 100 cm³ of 1M hydrochloric acid in separate thermos flasks. Record the temperature in each flask. Add the acid to the alkali and record the highest temperature observed. Using the equation $\Delta H = c \times m \times \Delta T$, calculate $\Delta H_1$, $\Delta H_2$ and $\Delta H_3$ and use the values obtained to verify Hess's Law.

2   Repeat the experiment, but use 100 cm³ of 1M sulphuric acid instead of the hydrochloric acid.

Compare the heats of neutralization obtained in **1** and **2**.

**Experiment 4**   Heat of solution.

Place 100 cm³ of water in a thermos flask and record the temperature. Weigh out about 10 g of anhydrous sodium carbonate accurately, add it to the water and stir. Record the highest temperature observed. Calculate the heat of solution for sodium carbonate in kJ mol⁻¹

**Experiment 5**   Heat of combustion.

Set up the apparatus shown below.

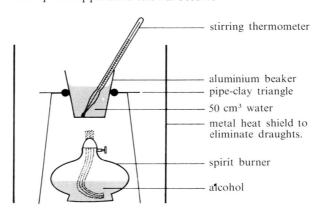

Weigh a spirit burner containing methanol. Record the temperature of the water in the beaker. Place the burner under the beaker and light the wick. When the temperature has risen by about 10°, extinguish the burner and record the highest temperature observed.

Reweigh the burner.

Repeat the experiment using ethanol, propan-1-ol, butan-1-ol and pentan-1-ol.

In each case calculate the heat of combustion of the alcohol.

|  | methanol | ethanol | propan-1-ol | butan-1-ol | pentan-1-ol |
|---|---|---|---|---|---|
| final temperature of water °C |  |  |  |  |  |
| initial temperature of water °C |  |  |  |  |  |
| $\Delta T$ |  |  |  |  |  |
| initial mass cf burner + alcohol g |  |  |  |  |  |
| final mass of burner − alcohol g |  |  |  |  |  |
| mass of alcohol used g |  |  |  |  |  |

For each of the alcohols, calculate the heat of combustion in $kJ\ mol^{-1}$. How do your results compare with the values given in Data table E1? How do your results confirm that these alcohols belong to the same homologous series?

## Chapter 5

**Experiment 1**   Electrode potentials (carbon standard).

Set up the apparatus shown on page 55, Figure 5.3, and measure the electrode potentials for a number of metals. Tabulate your results. Compare your results with standard $E°$ values and then compare individual differences in your table with individual differences in $E°$ values.

| Metal | Experimental p.d. V | $E°$ V |
|---|---|---|

**Experiment 2**   Electrode potentials (carbon standard)

Set up the apparatus shown in the diagram.

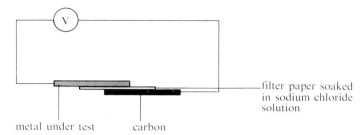

metal under test          carbon

filter paper soaked
in sodium chloride
solution

Use the same metals as for experiment 1 and again compare the individual differences.
Your teacher may demonstrate that this arrangement can be used for very reactive metals like sodium and potassium, but it is too dangerous for pupils to attempt.

**Experiment 3**   Oxidation and reduction.

Dissolve some crystals of iron(II) ammonium sulphate in dilute sulphuric acid and add this solution to a very dilute solution of potassium manganate(VII). Observe the colour change.
Write electron half-equations and hence the complete redox equation.

**Experiment 4**   Oxidation and reduction.

Boil a few copper turnings in 2 cm³ concentrated sulphuric acid **(care)** in a test-tube for five minutes. **Allow the test-tube to cool** and pour the contents carefully into about 50 cm³ of water. Note the colour of the solution. Write electron half-equations and hence the complete redox equation.

**Experiment 5**   Oxidizing agents.

Add sodium sulphite solution to each of the following solutions:

1   Potassium manganate(VII) solution acidified with dilute sulphuric acid.
2   Potassium dichromate(VI) solution acidified with dilute sulphuric acid.
3   Bromine water.

Note the colour changes.
Write electron half-equations and hence the complete redox equation for each reaction.

## Chapter 6

**Experiment 1**   Preparation of oxides.

Burn samples of the following elements in oxygen:
magnesium, calcium, aluminium, carbon.
Test each of the products with moist pH paper.
Your teacher may demonstrate the reaction between sodium and oxygen.

**Experiment 2**    Amphoteric oxides.

1    To solutions of lead(II) nitrate and lead(II) ethanoate add a few drops of potassium iodide solution and observe the colour of the precipitate. What is this precipitate?

2    Warm some lead(II) oxide with moderately concentrated hydrochloric acid and filter off any excess lead(II) oxide.
To the warm filtrate add a few drops of potassium iodide solution and compare this result with that obtained in **1**.
Does this solution contain $Pb^{2+}(aq)$?

3    Boil a small quantity of lead(II) oxide with sodium hydroxide solution and filter off any excess lead(II) oxide.
To the warm filtrate add a few drops of potassium iodide solution.
Does the solution contain $Pb^{2+}(aq)$?

Attempt to write equations for the reactions in **2** and **3** and draw a conclusion about the nature of lead(II) oxide.

**Experiment 3**    Preparation of chlorides.

Demonstration experiment. Using gas jars of chlorine and samples of lithium and sodium prepare samples of the ionic chlorides.

**Experiment 4**    Structure of chlorides.

Using models build the structures of sodium chloride and caesium chloride. Compare the structures.

**Experiment 5**    Preparation of the halogens. (A fume-cupboard **must** be used.)

1    Chlorine
Set up the apparatus shown in the diagram.

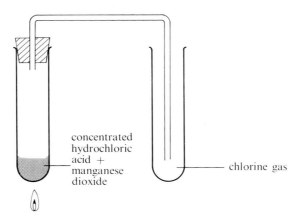

The tube is heated and chlorine gas is obtained. It is collected by the upward displacement of air since it is denser than air. What colour is the gas?
Test the gas with moist pH paper.

**2**   Bromine and iodine.

These halogens may be prepared in a similar way.
Add potassium bromide or potassium iodide to a few cm³ of dilute
sulphuric acid. Then add manganese dioxide to the test-tube and, using the
apparatus as for chlorine, prepare samples of bromine and iodine.

**Experiment 6**   Preparation of hydrogen halides.

**1**   Hydrogen chloride.

Set up the apparatus shown below.

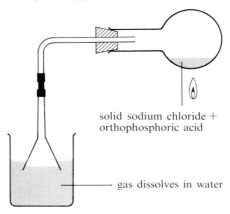

solid sodium chloride +
orthophosphoric acid

gas dissolves in water

Heat the tube gently. Any acid formed will dissolve in the water.
Test the pH of the solution.
Add silver(I) nitrate solution to the beaker and note the colour of the
precipitate.
What property of phosphoric acid is being used in this experiment?

**2**   Hydrogen bromide and hydrogen iodide.

These can be prepared in a similar fashion to hydrogen chloride, by using
sodium bromide and sodium iodide instead of sodium chloride.

**Experiment 7**   Action of $AgNO_3(aq)$ on halides

Place a few cm³ of sodium chloride, sodium bromide, and sodium iodide
solutions each in three separate test-tubes.
To each tube add a few cm³ of dilute nitric acid.
Now add 1 cm³ of silver(I) nitrate solution to each tube.
Record your results in a table.

| Halide solution | Colour of silver(I) halide precipitate | Solubility in dilute aqueous ammonia |
|---|---|---|
| Sodium chloride | | |
| Sodium bromide | | |
| Sodium iodide | | |

How could you use the results of this experiment to distinguish between the halides?

**Experiment 8**    Displacement reactions of the halogens.

Place 2 cm³ of solutions of sodium chloride, sodium bromide, and sodium iodide each in three separate test-tubes.
To each tube add 2 cm³ of trichloromethane (chloroform) and two drops of freshly prepared chlorine water. Shake the tubes.
Record your observations in a table.

| Halide | Colour in the trichloromethane layer |
| --- | --- |

What are the colours in the trichloromethane layer?
By considering standard reduction electrode potentials, offer an explanation for each of the reactions.

**Experiment 9**    Oxidizing action of the halogens.

Make up a dilute solution of sodium sulphite. Test a portion to ensure that the sulphate ion is absent.
To the sulphite solution add a few cm³ of bromine water and shake it.
What happens to the red/brown colour?
Write an electron half-equation to explain your answer.
Test the solution again for the presence of the sulphate ion.
What would this result seem to indicate?

Carry out a similar procedure with the following (use any necessary chemical tests to determine what is happening):

1    Chlorine water and sodium sulphite solution.
2    Bromine water and iron(II) sulphate solution.
3    Iodine in aqueous potassium iodide and sodium sulphite solution.

Are the halogens oxidizing or reducing agents?

**Experiment 10**    Discharge voltage of halide ions.

Set up the circuit shown in the diagram.

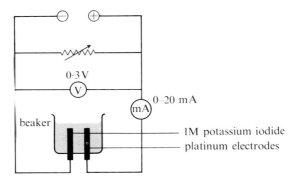

Platinum electrodes must be used in this experiment.
Make up 1M solutions of potassium iodide, potassium bromide and potassium chloride.
The variable resistor should have a range up to 500 ohms.
Place the potassium iodide solution in the beaker and adjust the variable resistor until a reading is obtained on the milliammeter. Note the voltage at this time.
Continue adjusting the variable resistor and so obtain a series of readings. Draw a graph of current (mA) against voltage.
Repeat the experiment using 1M potassium bromide and 1M potassium chloride. Plot all the results on the same piece of graph paper.

1    Compare the mA readings for each of the solutions at a constant voltage.

2    Compare the voltages required to produce a constant milliammeter reading for each solution.

3    Use your results to discuss the relative strengths of HI, HBr and HCl.

## Chapter 7

**Experiment 1**    The same rate?

Carry out each of the following reactions:

1    Add 10 cm³ of 0.1M hydrochloric acid to 10 cm³ of 0.1M sodium hydroxide in the presence of two drops of universal indicator solution.

2    Add 0.2 g of magnesium to 20 cm³ of 1M hydrochloric acid.

3    Place some iron filings in a test-tube and leave the tube open to the air.

Compare the rate of reaction in **1**, **2**, and **3**.
What conclusion can you come to about the rate of reaction?

**Experiment 2**    Effect of particle size on reaction rate.

Set up two beakers, one containing 1 g of powdered chalk and the other containing 1 g of lump chalk. To each beaker add 25 cm³ of 1M hydrochloric acid.
Which reaction finishes first?
How can you use your results to relate particle size and reaction rate?

**Experiment 3**    Effect of concentration on reaction rate.

$$S_2O_3^{2-}(aq) + 2H^+(aq) \rightarrow H_2O(l) + SO_2(g) + S(s)$$

Sulphur is produced during this reaction. We measure the time taken for the precipitated colloidal sulphur to reach a given intensity. To do this a cross is marked on a piece of paper and the time taken for the cross to be obscured is noted.

Prepare the following solutions:
1 litre of 0.25M sodium thiosulphate solution.
100 cm³ of 1M hydrochloric acid.

Place 200 cm³ of the sodium thiosulphate solution in a beaker and add 10 cm³ of the hydrochloric acid. Start a stopclock. Stir the mixture and note the time taken for the cross to be obscured.

Repeat the experiment with different volumes of the sodium thiosulphate solution, in each case made up to 200 cm³ with water. The same volume of acid is added in each case. The time taken for the cross to be obscured is noted and the reciprocal of the time is taken as a measure of the rate of reaction. Complete the table of results.

| Volume of sodium thiosulphate solution (cm³) | Volume of water (cm³) | Relative concentration of thiosulphate solution | Time t (s) | Rate $\frac{1}{t}$ (s⁻¹) × 10³ |
|---|---|---|---|---|
| 200 | 0 | 5 | | |
| 160 | 40 | 4 | | |
| 120 | 80 | 3 | | |
| 80 | 120 | 2 | | |
| 40 | 160 | 1 | | |

Plot a graph of $\frac{1}{t} \times 10^3$ against relative concentration.

Use your graph to show the relationship between reaction rate and concentration.

**Experiment 4**   Effect of temperature on reaction rate.

We shall again consider the reaction between sodium thiosulphate and dilute hydrochloric acid.

Prepare the following solutions:

100 cm³ 0.25M sodium thiosulphate solution.

100 cm³ 1M hydrochloric acid.

Dilute 10 cm³ of the sodium thiosulphate solution to 50 cm³ with water in a 100 cm³ beaker.

Stand a test-tube containing 5 cm³ of the hydrochloric acid in the beaker and heat to 30 °C.

Add the acid to the sodium thiosulphate solution, at the same time starting a stopclock. Place the beaker over a cross marked on a piece of paper and stir.

Note the time for the cross to be obscured.

Repeat the experiment for a range of temperatures up to 60 °C.

Record your results in a table.

Draw a graph of $\frac{1}{t} \times 10^3$ against temperature in °C.

**Experiment 5**   The iodine 'clock' reaction in the persulphate/iodide system.

The persulphate ion is a strong oxidizing agent $\quad S_2O_8^{2-} + 2e \rightarrow 2SO_4^{2-}$

and the iodide ion is a strong reducing agent $\quad 2I^- - 2e \rightarrow I_2$

*Solution 1* Dissolve approximately 4 g of potassium persulphate in water and make the solution up to 1 litre with water.

*Solution 2* Dissolve approximately 30 g of potassium iodide in water, add 10 cm³ of freshly prepared starch solution and make the solution up to 1 litre with water.

Put 5 cm³ of each solution into a test-tube and note the blue colour produced, indicating the presence of iodine. In order to determine the rate of reaction, we require to slow down the appearance of the blue colour and this is done by adding a crystal of sodium thiosulphate, a reducing agent, to solution 2. Mix equal volumes of solution 1 and solution 2 and note the time required to use up the thiosulphate, that is, the time for free iodine to give a blue colour with starch.

$$2S_2O_3^{2-} - 2e \rightarrow S_4O_6^{2-}$$
thiosulphate        dithionate
ion                 ion

1   Effect of temperature.

Set up the apparatus shown below.

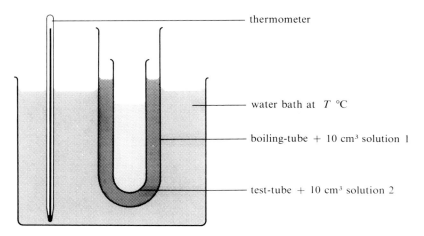

Pour the contents of the test-tube into the boiling tube. Start the clock and note the time taken for the blue colour to appear at the given temperature.

Repeat the experiment at different temperatures and make a table of temperatures and times taken.

**a)** Plot a graph of time against temperature.

**b)** Plot a graph of rate ($\frac{1}{t} \times 10^3$) against temperature.

2   Effect of concentration.

By again using the persulphate/iodide reaction, we can study the effect of concentration on the rate of reaction. Solutions 1 and 2 are those used in the first part of experiment 5.

Place 10 cm³ of solution 1 in a boiling tube and add 10 cm³ of solution 2.

Note the time taken for the blue colour to appear.

Repeat the procedure but vary the volume of solution 2 as shown in the table below. Record your results.

| Volume of solution 1 $S_2O_8^{2-}$ cm³ | Volume of solution 2 $I^-$ cm³ | Volume of water added cm³ | Relative concentration of solution 2 $(I^-)$ | Time $t$ seconds | Rate $\frac{1}{t}(s^{-1}) \times 10^3$ |
|---|---|---|---|---|---|
| 10 | 10 | 0 | 10 | | |
| 10 | 9 | 1 | 9 | | |
| 10 | 8 | 2 | 8 | | |
| 10 | 7 | 3 | 7 | | |
| 10 | 6 | 4 | 6 | | |
| 10 | 5 | 5 | 5 | | |
| 10 | 4 | 6 | 4 | | |
| 10 | 3 | 7 | 3 | | |
| 10 | 2 | 8 | 2 | | |
| 10 | 1 | 9 | 1 | | |
| 10 | 0 | 10 | 0 | $\infty$ | 0 |

a) What is the purpose of adding water?
b) Plot a graph of relative concentration of $I^-$ against the rate of reaction.
c) In a similar way, repeat the experiment but hold the volume of solution 2 constant and vary the volume of solution 1. Record your results in a table.
d) Plot a graph of relative concentration of $S_2O_8^{2-}$ against the rate of reaction.
e) Comment on the slope of both the graphs.

**Experiment 6**   Effect of concentration on equilibrium.

$$NH_3(g) + H_2O(l) \rightleftharpoons NH_4^+(aq) + OH^-(aq)$$

Add sufficient aqueous ammonia to 100 cm³ of water to give a pH of about 12.
Add some solid ammonium chloride to the solution. Check the pH.
Account for any differences in the pH readings.

**Experiment 7**   Effect of concentration on equilibrium.

$$Fe^{3+}(aq) + CNS^-(aq) \rightleftharpoons FeCNS^{2+}(aq)$$
yellow-brown                           red

Add small quantities of dilute solutions of iron(III) alum and potassium thiocyanate to a beaker full of water to produce an orange colour.
Split the solution between four beakers A, B, C, and D. Retain A as a control.
To B, add a little iron(III) alum.
To C, add a little solid potassium thiocyanate.
To D, add a little solid ammonium chloride. The chloride ion removes iron(III) ions to form a complex ion.
Record your results for B, C, and D.
Account for your results in terms of concentration changes affecting the equilibrium position.

**Experiment 8**   Effect of temperature on equilibrium.

Add a small piece of copper turning to a few cubic centimetres of concentrated nitric acid in a density bottle. The bottle fills with a brown gas. Place the bottle in (a) ice, (b) water at 30 °C, (c) water at 60 °C. Note the changes in colour. Explain your results.

**Experiment 9**   Bromination of heptane.

Place 5 cm³ of heptane in each of two test-tubes. To each tube add 2 cm³ of a solution of bromine dissolved in 1,2-dichloroethane. Wrap one tube in aluminium foil so that light is completely excluded. Expose both tubes to direct sunlight or ultra-violet light for twenty minutes. Examine the contents of each tube and give an explanation of your observations.

**Experiment 10**   Light and silver chloride.

Add equal amounts of sodium chloride solution to two test-tubes. To each tube add sufficient silver(I) nitrate solution to precipitate the silver(I) chloride. Wrap one tube in aluminium foil so that light is completely excluded. Expose both tubes to direct sunlight or u.v. light for some time. Examine the contents of each tube and give an explanation for your observations.

**Experiment 11**   The effect of a catalyst on the reaction rate.

Add 50 cm³ of hydrogen peroxide to each of two 1000 cm³ measuring cylinders. To each cylinder add 2 cm³ of detergent and then add about 2 g of manganese dioxide to one of the cylinders. Compare the reaction rate in the two cylinders. The manganese dioxide can be recovered by filtration.

**Experiment 12**   The effect of a catalyst on the reaction rate.

1   Dissolve 7 g of potassium sodium tartrate (Rochelle salt) in 60 cm³ of water and add to the solution 20 cm³ of 20-volume hydrogen peroxide.

2   Repeat the procedure above but this time add sufficient cobalt(II) chloride to make the solution pink in colour.

3   Heat both solutions and observe what happens.

How do the results of the experiment show:
   **a)**  that a catalyst can affect the rate of reaction?
   **b)**  that the catalyst is unchanged at the end of the reaction?

## Chapter 8

In all the following experiments safety glasses should be worn, and in certain cases it will be necessary to do the experiments in a fume cupboard.

**Experiment 1**   Preparation of methane.

Set up the apparatus as shown in the diagram.

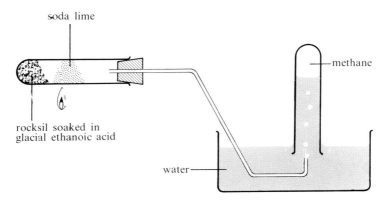

Describe the product and test its ease of combustion and reaction with bromine water.

**Experiment 2**   Preparation of ethene.

Set up the apparatus as shown in the diagram.

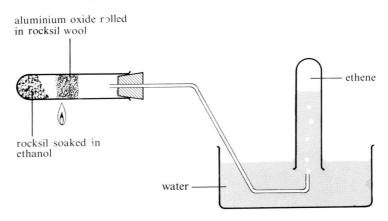

Describe the product and test its ease of combustion and reaction with bromine water.

**Experiment 3**   Using models, build as many structures as you can for the compound $C_4H_8$. Name the isomers produced.

**Experiment 4**   Preparation of ethyne.

Set up the apparatus as shown in the diagram.

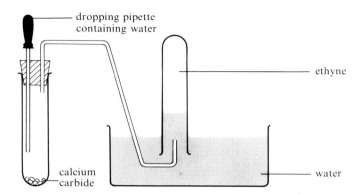

Describe the product and test its ease of combustion and reaction with bromine water.

Collect one third of a test-tube of ethyne and allow air to fill the rest of the test-tube. Compare the way in which the mixture burns with the way in which pure ethyne burns.

**Experiment 5**   Properties of aromatic hydrocarbons.

**1**   Combustion.
Place two to three drops of toluene in an evaporating basin in a fume cupboard. Set fire to the toluene and note the way in which it burns.

**2**   Reaction with bromine water.
Shake two to three drops of toluene with bromine water and note your observations.
From the results of these tests, and given that the molecular formula of toluene is $C_7H_8$, draw the structural formula for toluene.

**Chapter 9**

In all the following experiments safety glasses should be worn, and in certain cases it will be necessary to do the experiments in a fume cupboard.

**Experiment 1**   Preparation of ethanol

**1**   Fermentation
Add a paste of yeast to a solution of glucose in a test-tube. Incubate the test-tube for twenty-four hours at a temperature of 313 K (40 °C).
Add two glass beads to the test-tube and distil the mixture as shown.

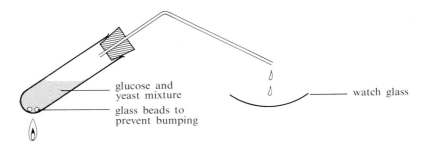

The first few drops of the distillate should be collected.
Heat a small piece of copper wire in a blue Bunsen flame until it is
black and drop it into the distillate. Explain what you see.

2   From an alkyl halide.
To 1 cm³ of ethyl bromide add 1 cm³ of dilute nitric acid and 2 cm³ of
dilute silver(I) nitrate solution. Shake the mixture and warm it in a
water-bath.
Does a precipitate of silver(I) bromide form?
Are there bromide ions present in ethyl bromide?

To 1 cm³ of ethyl bromide, add 2 cm³ of dilute sodium hydroxide solution
and boil for several minutes. Acidify the solution with dilute nitric acid
and add 2 cm³ of silver(I) nitrate solution.
Does a precipitate of silver(I) bromide form?
Are there bromide ions present in the solution?

Give an explanation for the results you have obtained.

**Experiment 2**   Properties of alcohols.

1   With sodium.
**Warning.** Sodium metal is dangerous and must be handled with care.
Place a small pellet of sodium in a little ethanol in a test-tube and collect
a sample of the gas evolved. Test the gas with a lighted taper.
a) Write an equation for the formation of the gas.
b) Write an equation for the action of sodium with water.
c) Compare these two equations.

2   With phosphorus pentachloride.
**Warning.** The fumes from phosphorus pentachloride are dangerous. Wear
safety glasses and do the test in a fume cupboard.
Add some water to one test-tube and some ethanol to another.
Carefully add a little phosphorus pentachloride to each tube and compare
the reactions.
Test the fumes evolved with moist pH paper and a glass rod dipped in
ammonia solution.
Write equations for the two reactions and also for the reaction of the
product with ammonia vapour.

3   With organic acids.
Put 2 cm³ of ethanol and 1 cm³ of glacial ethanoic acid in a boiling tube
and mix well. Carefully add a few drops of concentrated sulphuric acid
and warm in a water-bath for five minutes. Smell the product cautiously.
Write an equation for the reaction.

**Experiment 3**   Oxidation of ethanol.

**1**   With copper(II) oxide.
Roast a piece of copper foil in a bunsen flame until it gets a coating of black copper(II) oxide. Drop the warm foil into a little ethanol in an evaporating basin and note any changes which take place.
Smell the product cautiously.

**2**   With acidified dichromate(VI) solution.
Carefully add about 1 cm³ of concentrated sulphuric acid to 2 cm³ of potassium dichromate(VI) solution in a boiling tube. Shake the mixture and cool it under a tap. Add 1 cm³ of ethanol and note any changes which take place.
Smell the product cautiously.

**Experiment 4**   Oxidation of alcohols.

Alcohols can be oxidized by copper(II) oxide using the following apparatus.

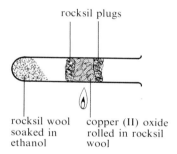

Heat the copper(II) oxide only—this should be sufficient to vaporize the alcohol.
Hold a piece of moist pH paper at the mouth of the tube.
Smell the product cautiously.

**Experiment 5**   Properties of phenol.

**Warning.** Phenol must not be allowed to come in contact with the skin as it is corrosive and is absorbed through the skin.

**1**   With water.
Dissolve some phenol in water and test the pH of the solution.
Write an equation for the reaction.

**2**   Neutralization.
Make a solution of phenol in water and add two drops of litmus indicator. Add sodium hydroxide solution dropwise, shaking between each addition, until the solution is neutral.
Write an equation for the reaction.

**3**   Displacement.
To the neutral or just-alkaline solution from (**2**) add some dilute hydrochloric acid.
Smell the solution to identify the product. Write an equation for the reaction between dilute hydrochloric acid and sodium phenoxide.

4    With chlorine.
     Dissolve some phenol in chlorine water and observe the characteristic
     odour of trichlorophenol (T.C.P.).

5    With sodium carbonate.
     Dissolve some phenol in water and add sodium carbonate. Record your
     observations.

6    Combustion.
     Set fire to a few crystals of phenol and describe the reaction.


**Experiment 6**    Similarities between aldehydes and ketones.

1    Addition of sodium hydrogensulphite.
     Shake three drops of (a) ethanal and (b) propanone with a saturated
     aqueous solution of sodium hydrogensulphite and note the white crystalline
     products which are formed.

2    Condensation with 2,4-dinitrophenylhydrazine.
     Add approximately 4 cm$^3$ of (a) ethanal and (b) propanone to a few
     drops of 2,4-dinitrophenylhydrazine dissolved in dilute hydrochloric acid
     and note the yellow precipitates which are formed.


**Experiment 7**    Differences between aldehydes and ketones.

1    Heat 2 cm$^3$ of (a) ethanal and (b) propanone with Benedict's reagent (or
     Fehling's A and B) in a boiling water-bath for about five minutes.
     A red precipitate indicates reduction.

2    Add a few drops of (a) ethanal and (b) propanone to some freshly
     prepared ammoniacal silver(I) nitrate solution in a clean text-tube.
     A brown precipitate or a silver mirror indicates reduction.


**Experiment 8**    Properties of carboxylic acids.

1    With metals.
     Compare the reactions of magnesium with dilute ethanoic acid and with
     dilute hydrochloric acid.
     Write equations for the reactions.

2    pH.
     Compare the pH of 0.1M ethanoic acid with that of 0.1M hydrochloric
     acid.

3    With carbonates.
     Add some dilute ethanoic acid to some sodium carbonate. Describe the
     reaction and attempt to identify the gas which is evolved.
     How could you distinguish between a carboxylic acid and a phenol?

4    Conductivity.
     Set up a conductivity cell and circuit. Obtain a reading with 1M
     hydrochloric acid. Without altering the apparatus replace the hydrochloric
     acid with 1M ethanoic acid.
     Account for the difference in conductivity.

**Experiment 9**   Constitution of ethanoic acid.

1   Phosphorus pentachloride. (**Care**—use a fume-cupboard.)
Test a sample of ethanoic acid with phosphorus pentachloride.
What conclusion can you draw from this reaction?

2   2,4-dinitrophenylhydrazine.
Test a sample of ethanoic acid with 2,4-dinitrophenylhydrazine.
What conclusion can you draw from this reaction?

**Experiment 10**   The structure of methanoic acid.

Test both methanoic acid and ethanoic acid with Benedict's reagent and
ammoniacal silver(I) nitrate as described in Experiment 7.
Bearing in mind that these reagents are tests for reducing agents like
aldehydes, attempt to give an explanation for your observations.

**Experiment 11**   Preparation of esters.

From a selection of alcohols and acids, attempt to make some esters,
using the method outlined in Experiment 2.3 on page 169.
Ethyl butanoate: pineapple oil
Pentyl ethanoate: pear drops
Methyl salicylate: oil of wintergreen

**Experiment 12**   Hydrolysis of esters.

Set up the apparatus shown in the diagram.

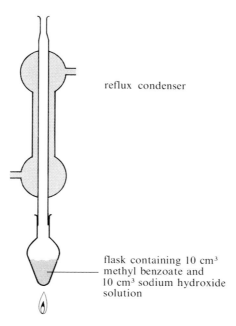

reflux condenser

flask containing 10 cm³
methyl benzoate and
10 cm³ sodium hydroxide
solution

Place 10 cm$^3$ of methyl benzoate and 10 cm$^3$ of dilute sodium hydroxide in the flask and reflux for thirty minutes.
Allow the flask to cool and add dilute hydrochloric acid to the solution in the flask. Account for your observations.

**Experiment 13**    Comparison of ethylamine and ammonia.

Carry out the following tests on ethylamine and ammonia.

1    Smell—caution.

2    Salt formation.
Hold a glass rod which has been dipped in concentrated hydrochloric acid above the solutions.

3    Complex formation.
Add dropwise solutions of ammonia and ethylamine to copper(II) sulphate solution in separate test-tubes. Record your observations.

4    Displacement.
Warm small samples of ammonium chloride and ethylamine hydrochloride with dilute sodium hydroxide solution and test the vapour evolved with moist pH paper.

**Experiment 14**    pH of ammonia, ethylamine and aniline.

Compare the pH of ammonia, ethylamine and aniline by adding dilute sodium hydroxide to samples of each in test-tubes and hold moist pH paper at the mouth of each tube.
Attempt to explain your results.

# Miscellaneous exercises

**Exercise 1**    The production of phenol (hydroxybenzene).
Phenol is widely used in industry for the manufacture of plastics, dyestuffs and other useful products. For many years, coal tar was the major source of phenol but with increasing demand, new methods of production had to be found. The most modern method involves the catalytic alkylation of benzene with propene, forming the alkylated benzene known as cumene. The cumene then undergoes air oxidation at pH 7 to cumene hydroperoxide. This reaction is autocatalytic, so when the plant is operating normally the concentration of cumene hydroperoxide is kept at 10%. The cumene hydroperoxide is then 'split' by lowering the pH, the mixture is neutralized and the products are distilled. The reaction sequence is:

A simplified flow diagram is as follows:

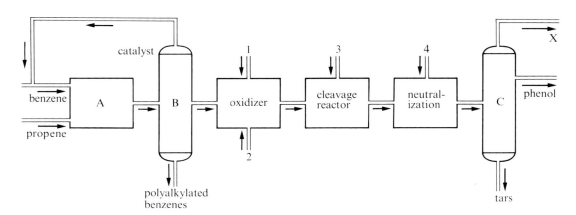

polyalkylated
benzenes

1 What is the primary industrial source of propene?
2 In the passage, what name is applied to the process occurring in A?
3 From the reaction sequence, what alternative name could be given to the process occurring in A?
4 From your understanding of the passage and the reaction sequence, what reagents must enter the flow diagram at (1), (2), (3) and (4)?
5 What distils from the top of column B?
6 Does this suggest anything about the relative quantities of benzene and propene in the original feedstock?
7 What is meant by the term 'autocatalytic'? What statement in the passage confirms your answer?
8 The profitability of the process depends upon recovery of the by-product X.
  8.1 Name this product.
  8.2 To what class of compound does it belong?
9 Draw the structural formula of a simple polyalkylated benzene which could be recovered from the bottom of column B.
10 Suggest what might happen to the 'tars' from the bottom of column C.
*SCEEB*

**Exercise 2** 1 Here is a scheme for the production of nitric acid from atmospheric nitrogen:

$$N_2 \xrightarrow{(1)} NO \xrightarrow{(2)} NO_2 \xrightarrow{(3)} HNO_3$$

The high cost of electricity makes stage (1) of this scheme uneconomic. Outline the modern industrial process for obtaining nitric oxide, NO, from atmospheric nitrogen.
2 Here is an experiment designed to illustrate the above scheme.

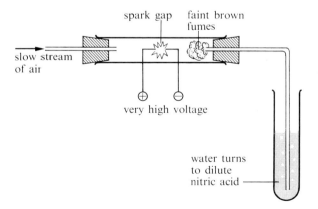

2.1 What is the purpose of the continual sparking?
2.2 How would you test the solution in the test-tube to show that it contains $H^+(aq)$ and $NO_3^-(aq)$?
(You need not give precise experimental details.)
2.3 Why do car exhaust fumes contain oxides of nitrogen?

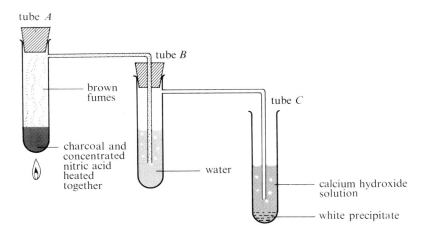

**3.1** Name the brown gas in tube *A*, and the gas which gives a white precipitate with the calcium hydroxide solution in tube *C*.

**3.2** Explain how these are produced by the reaction in tube *A*.

**3.3** Why do no brown fumes appear in tube *B*?

**3.4** If tube *B* is omitted and the gases from *A* are passed directly into calcium hydroxide solution no precipitate appears. Explain why not.

**4** 0.1 g of sulphur is heated with concentrated nitric acid. The sulphur is converted partly into sulphur dioxide, which escapes as a gas, and partly into $SO_4^{2-}$(aq) ions, which remain in the solution.

**4.1** How would you prove that the solution contains $SO_4^{2-}$(aq) ions?

**4.2** Suggest how you could extend this test so as to measure the quantity of $SO_4^{2-}$(aq) ions in the solution.

**4.3** Show how you would use the result from **4.2** to calculate the proportion of the original sulphur that had reacted to form $SO_4^{2-}$(aq).
*SCEEB*

**Exercise 3**  **1**  Of the elements of atomic number 3 to 10, choose one in each case which has a structure you would classify as

    **1.1**  metallic

    **1.2**  covalent, 'network' type,

    **1.3**  covalent, 'discrete molecules'.

**2**  Use the examples you have chosen for each of the three types and the relevant data in the Data tables (page 184) to support the following statement:

'A noteworthy difference between metallic and non-metallic elements (whether these are of "network" or "discrete molecule" type) is that the metals can exist as liquids over a wider range of temperature.'

**3**  State whether you would expect each of the following to conduct electricity appreciably when connected to a low voltage source.

    **3.1**  solid rubidium chloride

    **3.2**  liquid gallium (element 31)

    **3.3**  liquid nitrogen

Give your reason briefly in terms of the type of bonding present.

**4**

| Compound | Formula | Molecular weight | Boiling point |
|----------|---------|------------------|---------------|
| ethane | $CH_3CH_3$ | 30 | $-89\,°C$ |
| methanol | $CH_3OH$ | 32 | $64\,°C$ |
| hydrazine | $NH_2NH_2$ | 32 | $113\,°C$ |
| silane | $SiH_4$ | 32 | $-112\,°C$ |

**4.1**  From the information given, which of the compounds in the table contain hydrogen-bonding in the liquid state?

**4.2**  Why does hydrogen-bonding affect the boiling point of a substance?

**4.3**  In the table we have compared substances of similar molecular weight. Why is molecular weight significant in this case?

**4.4**  State *two* other ways in which the presence of hydrogen-bonding could affect the physical properties of a substance. *SCEEB*

**Exercise 4**  The Scottish chemist Joseph Black (1728–1799) is mainly remembered for his pioneer work on the gas which he called 'fixed air'. He found that 'fixed air' could be produced in several ways:

(a) By heating a compound of magnesium called 'magnesia alba', 'calcined magnesia' being left in the vessel.

(b) By adding a dilute acid to 'magnesia alba'.

(c) By the burning of charcoal.

(d) By the fermentation of glucose.

**1**    Deduce the modern names for 'fixed air', 'magnesia alba' and 'calcined magnesia'.

**2**    Write an equation for the reactions described in (b) and (d) above.

**3**    Black found that 12 parts by weight of magnesia alba left 5 parts by weight of calcined magnesia. By carrying out a suitable calculation, decide whether or not this was an accurate result.

**4**    Sea water contains 0.13% magnesium. The initial stage in the extraction of magnesium is the addition of alkali, which produces a precipitate of magnesium hydroxide. Outline the process by which magnesium metal is likely to be obtained from this precipitate, bearing in mind the following facts about magnesium compounds:

magnesium oxide: melting point 2800 °C
magnesium hydroxide: decomposes on heating
magnesium chloride: melting point 708 °C

**5**    A white powder is thought to be either magnesium hydride or magnesium oxide. Explain how adding cold water would enable you to decide which it is.

**6**    The crystal structure of an ionic compound is determined mainly by the 'radius ratio' of the ions involved:

$$\text{radius ratio} = \frac{\text{radius of cation}}{\text{radius of anion}}$$

By carrying out suitable calculations using information from the Data tables (page 188) in this book, explain why magnesium oxide is likely to have the same structure as sodium chloride. *SCEEB*

**Exercise 5**   Titanium

*Occurrence and extraction*
Titanium occurs in the form of the mineral rutile, $TiO_2$. Rutile can be converted to $TiCl_4$, a colourless liquid which boils at 136 °C and fumes in moist air. The $TiCl_4$ is heated with magnesium, and the mixture from this reaction is washed with very dilute acid, to leave titanium.

*Properties*
Titanium is resistant to corrosion by acid and by sea water, but will react if heated with fused alkali, to give substances called titanates, e.g. $K_2TiO_3$, potassium titanate.

*Uses*
Titanium is used in the aero-space industry and in chemical and marine engineering. Titanium carbide, TiC, is harder even than carborundum (silicon carbide) and finds many industrial uses.

Answer the following questions using the information about titanium contained in the above passage and the Data tables in this book.
**1**   Suggest a likely type of structure and bonding for the very hard substances, silicon carbide and titanium carbide.
**2**   From evidence in the passage what type of bonding do you think exists in titanium chloride? Give your reasons.
From information in the Data tables of this book, what formula and type of bonding might have been expected? Give your reasons.
**3**   Give an explanation for the fuming in moist air of titanium chloride.
**4**   What will be the products of the reaction between $TiCl_4$ and magnesium? What does this reaction suggest about the position of titanium, relative to magnesium, in the activity series?
Why is the mixture of products from the reaction 'washed with very dilute acid' to leave titanium metal?
**5**   Titanium reacts with alkali (as well as slightly with acids.) Name another metal which does this. What term is used to describe this property?
**6**   What *physical* property of titanium makes it suitable for use in the aero-space field? Quote your evidence for your answer. *SCEEB*

**Exercise 6**   **1**   The industrial preparation of methanol involves the combination of carbon monoxide and hydrogen using a zinc oxide catalyst according to the equation:

$$CO(g) + 2H_2(g) \rightleftharpoons CH_3OH(g)$$

The following graphs show the percentages of methanol in the reaction mixture under different conditions.

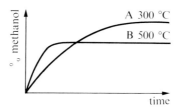

**1.1**   Why does graph *B* slope more steeply than graph *A* at the start?
**1.2**   Why do both graphs level off?
**1.3**   Is the reaction which produces methanol exothermic or endothermic? Explain how you arrive at your answer.

**1.4**  In industry, the reaction is usually carried out at 300 atmospheres pressure. Explain the use of high pressure.

**1.5**  Copy graph *B* into your answer book and using the same axes, draw a second graph to show how the percentage of methanol would have varied with time if no catalyst had been used.

**2**   When methanol vapour is passed over a heated aluminium oxide catalyst at 400 °C, dehydrogenation occurs according to the equation:

$$CH_3OH(g) \rightarrow CH_2O(g) + H_2(g)$$

**2.1**  Name the compound $CH_2O$.

**2.2**  It has been calculated that in this reaction, a small fraction of the methanol molecules react on their first impact with the catalyst surface. Draw a graph (no graph paper required) to represent the distribution of kinetic energy among methanol molecules in the vapour. (Label the horizontal axis 'energy' and the vertical axis 'fraction of molecules with particular energy'). Shade the area representing those molecules most likely to react on first impact. Give a brief explanation.

**3**   A pupil reads the following in a test-book:
'Hypochlorite ions ($ClO^-$) decompose in aqueous solution as follows:

$$2ClO^-(aq) \rightarrow 2Cl^-(aq) + O_2(g)$$

The reaction is catalysed by adding cobalt nitrate solution.'
Given a bottle containing hypochlorite ion solution and any chemicals he requires, what reactions could the pupil attempt to discover whether the catalytic activity is due to the cobalt ions or to the nitrate ions? *SCEEB*

**Exercise 7**   The following is adapted from a recent article in *The School Science Review*. 'Hats off to the thiosulphate ion ($S_2O_3^{2-}$)! This unique ion (selenium does not form an analogous one) provides much for us in the educational and photographic world. It is about the only agent suitable for removing unchanged silver halide from an exposed photographic film whilst not affecting the reduced silver; thus it is the universal "fixing agent". The instability of the acid $H_2S_2O_3$, which decomposes producing a precipitate of colloidal sulphur provides a reasonably slow reaction useful in the study of reaction rates.

Thiosulphate ion is a useful reducing agent, especially for iodine solution in volumetric analysis, being oxidised to $S_4O_6^{2-}$ by loss of electrons. Comparison of $S_2O_3^{2-}$ with sulphate ion ($SO_4^{2-}$) shows that:

(a) although the sulphate ion is a regular tetrahedron, $S_2O_3^{2-}$ is a distorted tetrahedron, the S—S bond being longer,

(b) the lattice energy of thiosulphate crystals is less than that of the corresponding sulphate crystals,

(c) barium thiosulphate is one of the most soluble barium salts known.'

**1**   The author implies that the $S_2O_3^{2-}$ ion is a very versatile reagent. List the uses mentioned in the passage.

**2**   What reaction does the passage suggest takes place when a photographic plate is exposed to light?

**3**   Given a solution of sodium thiosulphate how would you prepare a solution containing thiosulphuric acid? What would you expect to see happening to this solution?

4    From the information in the passage write a half-reaction equation for the reducing action of the thiosulphate ion. Write a corresponding half-reaction equation for the reduction of iodine.
5    Iodine solution was added a little at a time to sodium thiosulphate solution. Suggest a sensitive method which you would use to tell when the iodine solution was just in excess.
6    Draw a diagram showing the position of the atoms in a sulphate ion and in a thiosulphate ion.
7    Use the Data tables in this book to give an explanation of why the S—S bond is longer than the other bonds in the thiosulphate ion.
8    Does a high lattice energy normally indicate a high solubility?
9    A solution is suspected of containing either thiosulphate ions or sulphate ions. Explain how the addition of barium ions in solution would help you to decide. *SCEEB*

**Exercise 8**    The following is an extract from a lecture given by F. Soddy to a meeting of Nobel Prize-winners in Bavaria in 1952. *(Modern Science Memoirs No. 33)*.
'At that time, the turn of the century, the rare-earth elements had nearly all been separated from one another, a sequence, spread over no less than 40 units of atomic weight, of over a dozen different chemical elements, in point-blank contradiction to the chemical principle of the Periodic Law, so closely alike in chemical character that it is the work of a lifetime still to separate them. This had we known it, was a curious foreshadowing of one feature at least of isotopes, but in itself sufficient to contradict the original idea that it was the atomic weight that determined chemical character. Also showing the same thing was the fact, quite well established by the turn of the century, that there were definite exceptions to the Periodic Law, three pairs of elements being transposed, of which the most glaring was tellurium, atomic weight 127.6 preceding, not following, iodine, 126.9. At the time too it had been recognized that such a large proportion of the elements have atomic weights, so nearly integral in terms of that of oxygen as 16 (though there are plenty of others, like chlorine 35.453, straddling integers) that this could not be due to chance. This recalled Prout's then notorious but now famous hypothesis of 1815 that the elements were compounded of hydrogen, since many had nearly integral atomic weights in terms of that of hydrogen, and which the more exact atomic weight determinations of Stas and later atomic weight chemists had been considered completely to disprove.'
1    Why does Soddy suggest that the rare-earth elements are so difficult to separate?
2    What evidence is there in the passage that atomic weight does not determine chemical character?
3    In modern Periodic Tables iodine atomic weight 126.9 is placed after tellurium atomic weight 127.6.
Explain why this arrangement is *chemically* correct.
4    Why was it reasonable in 1815 for Prout to suggest that elements were composed of hydrogen?
5    What experimental evidence is given in the passage which might disprove Prout's suggestion?
6    How would modern atomic theory account for the atomic weight of chlorine as 35.453?
7    Explain why Prout's hypothesis can be viewed favourably in the light

of modern ideas on atomic theory.

**8**   In the passage, atomic weights are compared to oxygen as 16. What standard is now used for atomic weight determinations?

**9**   Name an apparatus used today to determine atomic weights.

**10**   In the determination of the atomic weight of element X the following analysis was obtained:

$$92.2\% \; _{14}^{28}X; \; 4.7\% \; _{14}^{29}X; \; 3.1\% \; _{14}^{30}X$$

Use these figures to calculate the atomic weight of element X. Show all the steps in your working clearly. *SCEEB*

**Exercise 9**   As we move horizontally across a period or vertically down a group in the Periodic Table, we can observe gradual changes in the physical and chemical properties of the elements.

Use the Data tables in this book to help you answer the following questions.

**1**   Where, between elements of atomic number 1 and 12, are the most abrupt changes in the chemical properties?

**2**   What *two* factors cause the tendency for the first ionization energy to increase as we move across a period?

**3**   Within the period sodium to argon, write formulae for

   **3.1**   the compound with the highest degree of ionic bonding;

   **3.2**   the hydride with the highest degree of covalent bonding.

**4**   By means of extended structural formulae, show why the group 4 elements carbon and silicon have dioxides which are totally different in character.

**5**   At ordinary temperatures, five distinct structures exist among the elements. These are:

closely packed molecules;
giant covalent structure;
giant ionic structure with interstitial electrons;
atomic gas;
molecular gas.

Which of these best describe the normal state of sulphur, silicon, argon, and aluminium?

**6**   Among simple compounds, the oxides probably show the most regular trends as we move across a period. In what sense can aluminium oxide be said to be intermediate in properties between the oxides of sodium and sulphur?

**7**   Mendeleef was able to predict many properties of elements yet to be discovered. Predict the physical appearance and estimate the melting points of

   **7.1**   francium

   **7.2**   astatine. *SCEEB*

**Exercise 10**   **1**   HOH          $C_3H_7OH$          NaOH          $C_6H_5OH$

These compounds all contain the —OH group. Explain:

   **1.1**   why a solution of NaOH conducts electricity but a solution of $C_3H_7OH$ does not;

   **1.2**   why a solution of $C_6H_5OH$ has a pH of less than 7 but a solution of NaOH has a pH of more than 7;

**1.3**   $C_3H_7OH$ and HOH react in a similar way with certain reagents. Select one such reagent and write an equation for its reaction with each.

**2**   Draw simple diagrams to show the shape of the molecules of methane and ethyne. Your diagram should show clearly the positions of the atoms in the molecule.
Explain briefly why the molecules have these shapes.

**3**   'Some of the reactions of phenylamine (aniline) are those of a substituted ammonia'.

**3.1**   What do you understand by this statement?

**3.2**   Dry hydrogen chloride was bubbled into phenylamine dissolved in ether and a precipitate was obtained. Name the precipitate and write an equation for the reaction.

**4**   When 0.16 g of an alcohol were burned in oxygen 0.22 g of carbon dioxide and 0.18 g of water were produced.

**4.1**   From the mass of water produced calculate the mass of hydrogen in the sample.

**4.2**   From the mass of carbon dioxide produced calculate the mass of carbon in the sample.

**4.3**   Deduce the mass of oxygen in the sample.

**4.4**   Find the empirical formula of the alcohol. *SCEEB*

# Data tables

**A**  **Periodic table**
atomic number, relative atomic mass, melting point, boiling point

**B**  **Electrochemical data**
electronegativity (Pauling symbol), 1st, 2nd, 3rd, and 4th ionization energy

**C**  **Atomic dimensions**
covalent radius, ionic radius

**D**  **Standard reduction electrode potentials**

**E**  **Thermochemical data**
1  Heats of combustion
2  Heats of sublimation
3  Specific heat capacity of water
4  Mean bond dissociation energies

Table A Periodic Table

| | | |
|---|---|---|
| | ———— | Symbol |
| **H** | 1 ———— | Atomic number |
| Hydrogen | ———— | Name |
| 1.008 | ———— | Relative atomic mass (Atomic weight) |
| 14 | ———— | Melting point K |
| 21 | ———— | Boiling point K |

| **Li** 3 | **Be** 4 |
|---|---|
| Lithium | Beryllium |
| 6.939 | 9.012 |
| 453 | 1551 |
| 1590 | 3243 |

| **Na** 11 | **Mg** 12 |
|---|---|
| Sodium | Magnesium |
| 22.990 | 24.312 |
| 371 | 922 |
| 1156 | 1363 |

| **K** 19 | **Ca** 20 | **Sc** 21 | **Ti** 22 | **V** 23 | **Cr** 24 | **Mn** 25 | **Fe** 26 | **Co** 27 |
|---|---|---|---|---|---|---|---|---|
| Potassium | Calcium | Scandium | Titanium | Vanadium | Chromium | Manganese | Iron | Cobalt |
| 39.100 | 40.080 | 44.956 | 47.900 | 50.942 | 51.996 | 54.938 | 55.847 | 58.933 |
| 337 | 1113 | 1814 | 1933 | 2163 | 2130 | 1517 | 1808 | 1768 |
| 1047 | 1757 | 3104 | 3560 | 3653 | 2945 | 2235 | 3023 | 3143 |

| **Rb** 37 | **Sr** 38 | **Y** 39 | **Zr** 40 | **Nb** 41 | **Mo** 42 | **Tc** 43 | **Ru** 44 | **Rh** 45 |
|---|---|---|---|---|---|---|---|---|
| Rubidium | Strontium | Yttrium | Zirconium | Niobium | Molybdenum | Technetium | Ruthenium | Rhodium |
| 85.470 | 87.620 | 88.905 | 91.220 | 92.906 | 95.940 | (99) | 101.070 | 102.905 |
| 312 | 1042 | 1796 | 2125 | 2741 | 2890 | 2445 | 2583 | 2239 |
| 961 | 1657 | 3610 | 4650 | 5015 | 4885 | 5150 | 4173 | 4000 |

| **Cs** 55 | **Ba** 56 | **La** 57 | **Hf** 72 | **Ta** 73 | **W** 74 | **Re** 75 | **Os** 76 | **Ir** 77 |
|---|---|---|---|---|---|---|---|---|
| Caesium | Barium | Lanthanum | Hafnium | Tantalum | Tungsten | Rhenium | Osmium | Iridium |
| 132.905 | 137.340 | 138.910 | 178.490 | 180.948 | 183.850 | 186.200 | 190.200 | 192.200 |
| 301 | 998 | 1193 | 2500 | 3269 | 3683 | 3453 | 3318 | 2683 |
| 951 | 1913 | 3727 | 4875 | 5698 | 5933 | 5900 | 5300 | 4403 |

| **Fr** 87 | **Ra** 88 | **Ac** 89 |
|---|---|---|
| Francium | Radium | Actinium |
| (223) | (226) | (227) |
| 300 | 202 | 1323 |
| 1050 | 211 | 3473 |

| Lanthanides | **La** 57 | **Ce** 58 | **Pr** 59 | **Nd** 60 | **Pm** 61 | **Sm** 62 | **Eu** 63 |
|---|---|---|---|---|---|---|---|
| | Lanthanum | Cerium | Praseodymium | Neodymium | Promethium | Samarium | Europium |
| | 138.910 | 140.120 | 140.907 | 144.240 | (147) | 150.350 | 151.960 |
| | 1193 | 1071 | 1004 | 1283 | 1353 | 1345 | 1095 |
| | 3727 | 3530 | 3485 | 3400 | 2733 | 2057 | 1873 |

| Actinides | **Ac** 89 | **Th** 90 | **Pa** 91 | **U** 92 | **Np** 93 | **Pu** 94 | **Am** 95 |
|---|---|---|---|---|---|---|---|
| | Actinium | Thorium | Protactinium | Uranium | Neptunium | Plutonium | Americium |
| | (227) | 232.038 | (231) | 238.030 | (237) | (242) | (243) |
| | 1323 | 2023 | > 1873 | 1405 | 913 | 914 | 1267 |
| | 3473 | 5063 | — | 4091 | 4175 | 4005 | 2880 |

| | | | | | |
|---|---|---|---|---|---|
| | | | | | **He**  2<br>Helium<br>4.003<br>1<br>4 |

| | | | | | |
|---|---|---|---|---|---|
| **B**  5<br>Boron<br>10.811<br>2573<br>2823 | **C**  6<br>Carbon<br>12.011<br>3823<br>5100 | **N**  7<br>Nitrogen<br>14.007<br>63<br>77 | **O**  8<br>Oxygen<br>16.000<br>55<br>90 | **F**  9<br>Fluorine<br>18.998<br>53<br>85 | **Ne**  10<br>Neon<br>20.183<br>24<br>27 |

| | | | | | |
|---|---|---|---|---|---|
| **Al**  13<br>Aluminium<br>26.982<br>933<br>2740 | **Si**  14<br>Silicon<br>28.086<br>1683<br>2628 | **P**  15<br>Phosphorus<br>30.974<br>317<br>553 | **S**  16<br>Sulphur<br>32.064<br>386<br>718 | **Cl**  17<br>Chlorine<br>35.453<br>172<br>238 | **Ar**  18<br>Argon<br>39.948<br>84<br>87 |

| | | | | | | | | |
|---|---|---|---|---|---|---|---|---|
| **Ni**  28<br>Nickel<br>58.710<br>1726<br>3005 | **Cu**  29<br>Copper<br>63.540<br>1356<br>2840 | **Zn**  30<br>Zinc<br>65.370<br>693<br>1180 | **Ga**  31<br>Gallium<br>69.720<br>203<br>2676 | **Ge**  32<br>Germanium<br>72.590<br>1210<br>3103 | **As**  33<br>Arsenic<br>74.922<br>1090<br>886 | **Se**  34<br>Selenium<br>78.960<br>490<br>958 | **Br**  35<br>Bromine<br>79.909<br>266<br>332 | **Kr**  36<br>Krypton<br>83.800<br>116<br>121 |

| | | | | | | | | |
|---|---|---|---|---|---|---|---|---|
| **Pd**  46<br>Palladium<br>106.400<br>1825<br>3413 | **Ag**  47<br>Silver<br>107.870<br>1235<br>2485 | **Cd**  48<br>Cadmium<br>112.400<br>594<br>1038 | **In**  49<br>Indium<br>114.820<br>430<br>2353 | **Sn**  50<br>Tin<br>118.690<br>505<br>2543 | **Sb**  51<br>Antimony<br>121.750<br>904<br>2023 | **Te**  52<br>Tellurium<br>127.600<br>723<br>1263 | **I**  53<br>Iodine<br>126.904<br>387<br>457 | **Xe**  54<br>Xenon<br>131.300<br>161<br>166 |

| | | | | | | | | |
|---|---|---|---|---|---|---|---|---|
| **Pt**  78<br>Platinum<br>195.090<br>2045<br>4100 | **Au**  79<br>Gold<br>196.967<br>1337<br>3080 | **Hg**  80<br>Mercury<br>200.590<br>234<br>630 | **Tl**  81<br>Thallium<br>204.370<br>577<br>2730 | **Pb**  82<br>Lead<br>207.190<br>601<br>2013 | **Bi**  83<br>Bismuth<br>208.980<br>544<br>1833 | **Po**  84<br>Polonium<br>(210)<br>527<br>1235 | **At**  85<br>Astatine<br>(210)<br>575<br>610 | **Rn**  86<br>Radon<br>(222)<br>202<br>211 |

| | | | | | | | |
|---|---|---|---|---|---|---|---|
| **Gd**  64<br>Gadolinium<br>157.250<br>1584<br>3506 | **Tb**  65<br>Terbium<br>158.924<br>1633<br>3314 | **Dy**  66<br>Dysprosium<br>162.500<br>1682<br>2608 | **Ho**  67<br>Holmium<br>164.930<br>1743<br>2993 | **Er**  68<br>Erbium<br>167.260<br>1795<br>2783 | **Tm**  69<br>Thulium<br>168.934<br>1818<br>2000 | **Yb**  70<br>Ytterbium<br>173.040<br>1097<br>1466 | **Lu**  71<br>Lutetium<br>174.970<br>1929<br>3588 |

| | | | | | | | |
|---|---|---|---|---|---|---|---|
| **Cm**  96<br>Curium<br>(247)<br>1613 | **Bk**  97<br>Berkelium<br>(249) | **Cf**  98<br>Californium<br>(251) | **Es**  99<br>Einsteinium<br>(254) | **Fm**  100<br>Fermium<br>(253) | **Md**  101<br>Mendelevium<br>(256) | **No**  102<br>Nobelium<br>(254) | **Lw**  103<br>Lawrencium<br>(257) |

## Table B Electrochemical data

| Symbol | Electro-negativity Pauling | Ionization energy kJ mol$^{-1}$ | | | |
|---|---|---|---|---|---|
| | | 1st | 2nd | 3rd | 4th |
| H | 2.1 | 1312 | | | |
| He | — | 2362 | 5250 | | |
| Li | 1.0 | 520 | 7297 | 11787 | |
| Be | 1.5 | 899 | 1757 | 14845 | 21003 |
| B | 2.0 | 801 | 2427 | 3659 | 25022 |
| C | 2.5 | 1086 | 2352 | 4620 | 6222 |
| N | 3.0 | 1402 | 2856 | 4577 | 7474 |
| O | 3.5 | 1314 | 3388 | 5296 | 7468 |
| F | 4.0 | 1681 | 3376 | 6045 | 8409 |
| Ne | — | 2080 | 3717 | 6128 | 9362 |
| Na | 0.9 | 496 | 4563 | 6920 | 9542 |
| Mg | 1.2 | 738 | 1450 | 7733 | 10546 |
| Al | 1.5 | 577 | 1816 | 2744 | 11576 |
| Si | 1.8 | 786 | 1577 | 3232 | 4353 |
| P | 2.1 | 1012 | 1903 | 2910 | 4956 |
| S | 2.5 | 999 | 2258 | 3378 | 4563 |
| Cl | 3.0 | 1255 | 2297 | 3850 | 5163 |
| Ar | — | 1520 | 2665 | 3647 | 5770 |
| K | 0.8 | 419 | 3070 | 4439 | 5877 |
| Ca | 1.0 | 590 | 1145 | 4942 | 6466 |
| Sc | 1.3 | 631 | 1235 | 2388 | 7131 |
| Ti | 1.5 | 658 | 1310 | 2651 | 4173 |
| V | 1.6 | 650 | 1414 | 2828 | 4632 |
| Cr | 1.6 | 653 | 1591 | 2987 | 4825 |
| Mn | 1.5 | 717 | 1509 | 3251 | 5018 |
| Fe | 1.8 | 759 | 1561 | 2957 | 5481 |
| Co | 1.8 | 758 | 1645 | 3232 | 8019 |
| Ni | 1.8 | 739 | 1751 | 3393 | |
| Cu | 1.9 | 745 | 1958 | 3554 | |
| Zn | 1.6 | 906 | 1733 | 3831 | |
| Ga | 1.6 | 579 | 1985 | 2963 | 6195 |
| Ge | 1.8 | 760 | 1537 | 3301 | 4314 |
| As | 2.0 | 947 | 1798 | 2735 | 4835 |
| Se | 2.4 | 941 | 2075 | 3088 | 4150 |
| Br | 2.8 | 1142 | 2084 | 3464 | 4564 |
| Kr | — | 1351 | 2370 | 3561 | 4198 |
| Rb | 0.8 | 403 | 2654 | 3860 | |
| Sr | 1.0 | 549 | 1064 | 4200 | 5501 |
| Y | 1.2 | 616 | 1180 | 1978 | |
| Zr | 1.4 | 660 | 1267 | 2218 | 3313 |
| Nb | 1.6 | 664 | 1382 | 2416 | 3696 |
| Mo | 1.8 | 685 | 1558 | 2618 | 4478 |
| Tc | 1.9 | 703 | 1473 | 2851 | |
| Ru | 2.2 | 711 | 1617 | 2746 | |
| Rh | 2.2 | 720 | 1744 | 2996 | |
| Pd | 2.2 | 804 | 1874 | 3177 | |

Table B continued

| Symbol | Electro-negativity Pauling | Ionization energy kJ mol$^{-1}$ | | | |
|--------|----------|------|------|------|------|
| | | 1st | 2nd | 3rd | 4th |
| Ag | 1.9 | 731 | 2073 | 3360 | |
| Cd | 1.7 | 868 | 1631 | 3616 | |
| In | 1.7 | 558 | 1820 | 2705 | 5250 |
| Sn | 1.8 | 709 | 1412 | 2942 | 3929 |
| Sb | 1.9 | 834 | 1592 | 2441 | 4256 |
| Te | 2.1 | 869 | 1795 | 2991 | 3667 |
| I | 2.5 | 1009 | 1846 | | |
| Xe | — | 1170 | 2046 | 3020 | 4053 |
| Cs | 0.7 | 376 | 2422 | 3378 | |
| Ba | 0.9 | 503 | 965 | 3426 | |
| La | 1.1 | 541 | 1103 | 1850 | |
| Hf | 1.3 | 676 | 1438 | 2239 | 3213 |
| Ta | 1.5 | 760 | 1563 | | |
| W | 1.7 | 770 | 1708 | | |
| Re | 1.9 | 759 | 1602 | | |
| Os | 2.2 | 820 | 1640 | | |
| Ir | 2.2 | 869 | | | |
| Pt | 2.2 | 869 | 1800 | | |
| Au | 2.4 | 890 | 1978 | | |
| Hg | 1.9 | 1006 | 1809 | 3300 | 4777 |
| Tl | 1.8 | 589 | 1970 | 2876 | 4893 |
| Pb | 1.8 | 716 | 1450 | 3081 | 4083 |
| Bi | 1.9 | 703 | 1610 | 2467 | 4371 |
| Po | 2.0 | 813 | | | |
| At | 2.2 | 917 | | | |
| Rn | — | 1037 | | | |
| Fr | 0.7 | 386 | | | |
| Ra | 0.9 | 509 | 979 | | |
| Ac | 1.1 | 666 | 1168 | 1930 | |

### Table C Atomic dimensions

| Symbol | Covalent radius nm(m × 10⁻⁹) | Ionic radius nm(m × 10⁻⁹) | Symbol | Covalent radius nm(m × 10⁻⁹) | Ionic radius nm(m × 10⁻⁹) |
|---|---|---|---|---|---|
| H  | 0.037 | 0.154 | Ag | 0.134 | 0.126 |
| He | —     | —     | Cd | 0.141 | 0.097 |
| Li | 0.123 | 0.068 | In | 0.150 | 0.081 |
| Be | 0.089 | .0.035 | Sn | 0.140 | 0.093 |
| B  | 0.080 | 0.023 | Sb | 0.141 | 0.245 |
| C  | 0.077 | 0.016 | Te | 0.137 | 0.211 |
| N  | 0.074 | 0.171 | I  | 0.133 | 0.220 |
| O  | 0.074 | 0.132 | Xe | —     | —     |
| F  | 0.072 | 0.133 | Cs | 0.235 | 0.167 |
| Ne | —     | —     | Ba | 0.198 | 0.134 |
| Na | 0.157 | 0.097 | La | 0.169 | 0.101 |
| Mg | 0.136 | 0.066 | Hf | —     | 0.078 |
| Al | 0.125 | 0.051 | Ta | 0.144 | 0.068 |
| Si | 0.117 | 0.042 | W  | 0.130 | 0.070 |
| P  | 0.110 | 0.212 | Re | 0.128 | 0.072 |
| S  | 0.104 | 0.184 | Os | 0.126 | 0.088 |
| Cl | 0.099 | 0.181 | Ir | 0.126 | 0.068 |
| Ar | —     | —     | Pt | 0.129 | 0.080 |
| K  | 0.203 | 0.133 | Au | 0.134 | 0.137 |
| Ca | 0.174 | 0.099 | Hg | 0.144 | 0.110 |
| Sc | 0.144 | 0.073 | Tl | 0.155 | 0.095 |
| Ti | 0.132 | 0.094 | Pb | 0.154 | 0.120 |
| V  | 0.122 | 0.088 | Bi | 0.152 | 0.098 |
| Cr | 0.117 | 0.089 | Po | —     | 0.067 |
| Mn | 0.117 | 0.080 | At | 0.140 | 0.062 |
| Fe | 0.116 | 0.074 | Rn | —     | —     |
| Co | 0.116 | 0.072 | Fr | —     | 0.180 |
| Ni | 0.115 | 0.069 | Ra | —     | 0.143 |
| Cu | 0.117 | 0.072 | Ac | —     | 0.118 |
| Zn | 0.125 | 0.074 |    |       |       |
| Ga | 0.125 | 0.062 |    |       |       |
| Ge | 0.122 | 0.053 |    |       |       |
| As | 0.121 | 0.222 |    |       |       |
| Se | 0.117 | 0.191 |    |       |       |
| Br | 0.114 | 0.196 |    |       |       |
| Kr | —     | —     |    |       |       |
| Rb | 0.216 | 0.147 |    |       |       |
| Sr | 0.191 | 0.112 |    |       |       |
| Y  | 0.162 | 0.089 |    |       |       |
| Zr | 0.145 | 0.109 |    |       |       |
| Nb | 0.134 | 0.100 |    |       |       |
| Mo | 0.129 | 0.093 |    |       |       |
| Tc | —     | 0.098 |    |       |       |
| Ru | 0.124 | 0.067 |    |       |       |
| Rh | 0.125 | 0.068 |    |       |       |
| Pd | 0.128 | 0.080 |    |       |       |

## Table D Standard reduction electrode potentials ($E°$).

| Half-cell reaction | | $E°$ V at 25 °C |
|---|---|---|
| $Li^+(aq) + e^- \rightarrow Li(s)$ | | $-3.05$ |
| $Rb^+(aq) + e^- \rightarrow Rb(s)$ | | $-2.93$ |
| $Cs^+(aq) + e^- \rightarrow Cs(s)$ | | $-2.92$ |
| $K^+(aq) + e^- \rightarrow K(s)$ | | $-2.92$ |
| $Ca^{2+}(aq) + 2e^- \rightarrow Ca(s)$ | | $-2.87$ |
| $Na^+(aq) + e^- \rightarrow Na(s)$ | | $-2.71$ |
| $Mg^{2+}(aq) + 2e^- \rightarrow Mg(s)$ | | $-2.34$ |
| $Al^{3+}(aq) + 3e^- \rightarrow Al(s)$ | | $-1.71$ |
| $2H_2O + 2e^- \rightarrow H_2(g) + 2OH^-(aq)$ | pH $= 7$ | $-0.83$ |
| $Zn^{2+}(aq) + 2e^- \rightarrow Zn(s)$ | | $-0.76$ |
| $Cr^{3+}(aq) + 3e^- \rightarrow Cr(s)$ | | $-0.74$ |
| $S(s) + 2e^- \rightarrow S^{2-}(aq)$ | | $-0.51$ |
| $Fe^{2+}(aq) + 2e^- \rightarrow Fe(s)$ | | $-0.41$ |
| $Cr^{3+}(aq) + e^- \rightarrow Cr^{2+}(aq)$ | | $-0.41$ |
| $Sn^{2+}(aq) + 2e^- \rightarrow Sn(s)$ | | $-0.14$ |
| $Pb^{2+}(aq) + 2e^- \rightarrow Pb(s)$ | | $-0.13$ |
| $Fe^{3+}(aq) + 3e^- \rightarrow Fe(s)$ | | $-0.04$ |
| $2H^+(aq) + 2e^- \rightarrow H_2(g)$ | pH $= 0$ | $0.00$ |
| $S(s) + 2H^+(aq) + 2e^- \rightarrow H_2S(aq)$ | | $0.14$ |
| $Sn^{4+}(aq) + 2e^- \rightarrow Sn^{2+}(aq)$ | | $0.15$ |
| $Cu^{2+}(aq) + e^- \rightarrow Cu^+(aq)$ | | $0.16$ |
| $SO_4^{2-}(aq) + 2H^+(aq) + 2e^- \rightarrow SO_3^{2-}(aq) + H_2O$ | | $0.20$ |
| $Hg_2Cl_2(s) + 2e^- \rightarrow 2Hg(l) + 2Cl^-(aq)$ | | $0.27$ |
| $Cu^{2+}(aq) + 2e^- \rightarrow Cu(s)$ | | $0.34$ |
| $O_2(g) + 2H_2O + 4e^- \rightarrow 4OH^-(aq)$ | pH $= 14$ | $0.40$ |
| $Cu^+(aq) + e^- \rightarrow Cu(s)$ | | $0.52$ |
| $I_2(s) + 2e^- \rightarrow 2I^-(aq)$ | | $0.54$ |
| $Fe^{3+}(aq) + e^- \rightarrow Fe^{2+}(aq)$ | | $0.77$ |
| $Ag^+(aq) + e^- \rightarrow Ag(s)$ | | $0.80$ |
| $2NO_3^-(aq) + 4H^+(aq) + 2e^- \rightarrow N_2O_4(g) + 2H_2O$ | | $0.81$ |
| $Hg^{2+}(aq) + 2e^- \rightarrow Hg(l)$ | | $0.85$ |
| $NO_3^-(aq) + 4H^+(aq) + 3e^- \rightarrow NO(g) + 2H_2O$ | | $0.96$ |
| $Br_2(l) + 2e^- \rightarrow 2Br^-(aq)$ | | $1.07$ |
| $MnO_2(s) + 4H^+(aq) + 2e^- \rightarrow Mn^{2+}(aq) + 2H_2O$ | | $1.21$ |
| $O_2(g) + 4H^+(aq) + 4e^- \rightarrow 2H_2O$ | | $1.23$ |
| $Cr_2O_7^{2-}(aq) + 14H^+(aq) + 6e^- \rightarrow 2Cr^{3+}(aq) + 7H_2O$ | | $1.33$ |
| $Cl_2(g) + 2e^- \rightarrow 2Cl^-(aq)$ | | $1.36$ |
| $Au^{3+}(aq) + 3e^- \rightarrow Au(s)$ | | $1.42$ |
| $MnO_4^-(aq) + 8H^+(aq) + 5e^- \rightarrow Mn^{2+}(aq) + 4H_2O$ | | $1.50$ |
| $Au^+(aq) + e^- \rightarrow Au(s)$ | | $1.68$ |
| $F_2(g) + 2e^- \rightarrow 2F^-(aq)$ | | $2.87$ |

**Table E Thermochemical data**

**Table E1**
Heats of combustion kJ mol$^{-1}$

| Alkanes | |
|---|---|
| $CH_4(g)$ | $-892$ |
| $C_2H_6(g)$ | $-1562$ |
| $C_3H_8(g)$ | $-2230$ |
| $C_4H_{10}(g)$ | $-2879$ |
| $C_5H_{12}(l)$ | $-3514$ |
| $C_6H_{14}(l)$ | $-4169$ |
| $C_7H_{16}(l)$ | $-4818$ |
| $C_8H_{18}(l)$ | $-5458$ |
| $C_{10}H_{22}(l)$ | $-6747$ |

| Alcohols | |
|---|---|
| $CH_3OH(l)$ | $-716$ |
| $C_2H_5OH(l)$ | $-1369$ |
| $C_3H_7OH(l)$ | $-2023$ |
| $C_4H_9OH(l)$ | $-2680$ |
| $C_5H_{11}OH(l)$ | $-3335$ |

| Alkenes | |
|---|---|
| $C_2H_4(g)$ | $-1413$ |
| $C_3H_6(g)$ | $-2054$ |
| $C_4H_8(g)$ | $-2723$ |

| Alkynes | |
|---|---|
| $C_2H_2(g)$ | $-1327$ |
| $C_3H_4(g)$ | $-1911$ |

| Elements | |
|---|---|
| $C(s)$ | $-394$ |
| $H_2(g)$ | $-286$ |

| Cycloalkanes | |
|---|---|
| $C_3H_6(g)$ | $-2095$ |
| $C_4H_8(l)$ | $-2724$ |
| $C_5H_{10}(l)$ | $-3296$ |
| $C_6H_{12}(l)$ | $-3925$ |

| Benzene | |
|---|---|
| $C_6H_6(l)$ | $-3272$ |

| Cyclohexene | |
|---|---|
| $C_6H_{10}(l)$ | $-3737$ |

**Table E3**
Specific heat capacity of water

4.2 J g$^{-1}$ K$^{-1}$

**Table E4**
Mean bond dissociation energies kJ mol$^{-1}$

| | |
|---|---|
| H—H | 437 |
| H—F | 569 |
| H—Cl | 432 |
| H—Br | 366 |
| H—I | 299 |
| H—O | 465 |
| H—N | 385 |
| C—C | 347 |
| C=C | 608 |
| C≡C | 830 |
| C=C  (Benzene) | 520 |
| C—H | 411 |
| C—O | 355 |
| C=O | 725 |
| C—N | 247 |
| C—F | 486 |
| C—Cl | 327 |
| C—Br | 280 |
| C—I | 210 |
| F—F | 155 |
| Cl—Cl | 240 |
| Br—Br | 193 |
| I—I | 151 |
| N≡N | 950 |

**Table E2**
Heats of sublimation kJ mol$^{-1}$

| | |
|---|---|
| $C(s) \rightarrow C(g)$ | 715 |

# Answers to numerical questions

## Chapter 1

| | |
|---|---|
| **1.1** | 50% of each |
| **2** | 28.11 |
| **3.2** | 24.7; magnesium |
| **4.2** | 10.81 |
| **6.2.1** | $SO_2$ |
| **8** | 16.03; oxygen |
| **9.2** | 44.15 |

## Chapter 2

| | |
|---|---|
| **2.1** | $x$ is $^{24}_{12}Mg$ |
| **2.2** | $y$ is $^{1}_{0}n$ |
| **5.1** | X is Ra; Y is Rn; Z is Po. |
| **5.2** | alpha particle |
| **7** | $p$ is 3; $q$ is 1; X is hydrogen (tritium) |
| **8.3.1** | $^{232}_{90}Th$ |
| **8.3.2** | $^{228}_{89}Ac$ |
| **9.1** | 6.5 g |

## Chapter 3

| | |
|---|---|
| **1** | 0.1 mole; 2.24 l chlorine gas |
| **2.6** | 0.01 |
| **3** | 28 |
| **4** | 352.8 cm³ |
| **5.1** | 381 g Cu |
| **5.2** | 44.8 l nitrogen |
| **6** | 16 |
| **7** | $3 \times 10^{23}$ molecules |
| **8** | $4 \times 10^{23}$ molecules |
| **9** | 44 |
| **10** | $48 \times 10^{23}$ |
| **11.1** | $SO_2$ |
| **12** | $1.304 \times 10^{17}$ |
| **13** | 2.24 l; $2.4 \times 10^{24}$ atoms |
| **14** | 19 300C |
| **15** | $Au^{3+}$; $AuCl_3$ |
| **16** | Nitrogen; $NaN_3$ |
| **17** | 24.27; magnesium |
| **18** | 58.01; $C_4H_{10}$ |
| **19** | 6.57 g |

## Chapter 4

| | |
|---|---|
| **1.1** | $+364$ kJ mol$^{-1}$ |
| **1.2** | $-55.5$ kJ |
| **3.1** | A is $+240$ kJ; B is $+5$ kJ; C is $-192$ kJ |
| **4.2** | $+709$ kJ |
| **5** | $-50$ kJ |
| **6** | $-462$ kJ |
| **7.1** | $-1605$ kJ |
| **7.2** | $+803$ kJ |
| **9** | $-128$ kJ |
| **10** | 298.4 kJ |
| **11** | $-316$ kJ |

## Chapter 5

| | |
|---|---|
| **2.2.1** | 1.56 V |
| **3.1.4** | 0.44 V |
| **8** | 0.74 V |

## Chapter 7

| | |
|---|---|
| **1.1.1** | 200 °C; 900 atmospheres |
| **1.1.3** | 33% |
| **6.1** | D |
| **6.2** | A |
| **6.3** | C + B |
| **8.1.2** | Activation energy $= +50$ kJ; $\Delta H = -40$ kJ |

## Chapters 8 and 9

| | |
|---|---|
| **3.4** | 252 g |
| **4.8** | 17.6 g; 73.9% |

## Miscellaneous exercise

| | |
|---|---|
| **8.10** | 28.109 |
| **10.4.1** | 0.02 g |
| **10.4.2** | 0.06 g |
| **10.4.3** | 0.08 g |
| **10.4.4** | $(CH_4O)_n$ |

# Index

All page numbers in heavy type refer to experiments.